A professional engineer with forty years of international manufacturing experience, **Fiona Erskine's** first graduate job was in the factory described in *Phosphate Rocks*. Born in Edinburgh, Fiona grew up riding motorbikes and jumping into cold water. After studying chemical engineering at university, she learned to weld, cast and machine with apprentices in Paisley. As a professional engineer she has worked and travelled internationally and is now based in the North East of England. Her first novel, *The Chemical Detective*, which was shortlisted for the Specsavers Debut Crime Novel Award 2020, was followed by *The Chemical Reaction*.

PHOSPHATE ROCKS

A DEATH IN TEN OBJECTS

Fiona Erskine

SANDSTONE PRESS

First published in Great Britain in 2021
Sandstone Press Ltd
PO Box 41
Muir of Ord
IV6 7YX
Scotland

www.sandstonepress.com

Editor: Robert Davidson

Sandstone Press is committed to a sustainable future. This book
is made from Forest Stewardship Council ® certified paper.

ISBN: 978-1-913207-52-6
ISBNe: 978-1-913207-53-3

Cover design by Kidethic
Typography by Iolaire, Newtonmore
Printed in the UK by Severn, Gloucester

To John Gibson

Perfection belongs to narrated events,
not to those we live.

<small>PRIMO LEVI</small>, *The Periodic Table*

Contents

Introduction

In early 1988, I was rattling down Leith Walk on my Honda 90 motorbike (0–11 miles per hour in 1 millisecond, although it took longer to get above 11) towards Edinburgh's dockland and the Scottish Agricultural Industries (SAI) fertiliser factory. I could tell what sort of shift it was going to be from the factory chimneys. My last one.

Five years previously, when I first informed the deputy manager that I planned to work shifts like the male graduates, he paled. A five-foot-three-and-a-half, sixty-kilo, twenty-something, cocky, over-educated feminist alone at night in a factory of hundreds of big, rough men... he was terrified for them. So, he appointed a trusted, experienced shift foreman to keep me out of trouble: John Gibson.

Many years and several jobs later, after a skiing accident and an even more bruising first brush with fiction, I was persuaded by my partner in life to write down the stories I used to tell arriving home from a twelve-hour shift in Leith docks, caked in phosphate rock.

I embarked on NaNoWriMo (National Novel Writing Month) armed only with the words 'I remember', and it all poured out.

NaNoWriMo is a bit like a Honda 90. You can race ahead with extraordinary speed and exhilaration; tens of thousands of words can be knocked out in a month. Unfortunately, it took me almost a decade to knock that first draft into shape.

The person I found it hardest to write about was John, my mentor and shift companion – enigmatic, infuriating, charming, capricious, obstinate, kind and wise – until I found a way to illuminate him by putting him centre stage, where he belongs.

Like the shaggy dog stories that John shared to get us through a night shift, not all of what follows is exactly true. Names have been changed because the real people involved are still bigger than me. Dates have been changed because my memory is appalling.

I am going to pop up from time to time, like the James Gillespie's High School and Cambridge University educated smart arse I am, to explain some of the technical stuff. You'll be able to spot me by the thud of Perry's 4.46-kilogram *Chemical Engineering Handbook* (Version 6), the motes of dust (atishoo!) and the rustle of its 2,240 pages.

Inspired by Primo Levi, in the style of Dan Brown, this is the portrait of a factory in all its complex, glorious, interconnected, messy entirety. A hymn to the forgotten, the unknown and the misunderstood, this is the story of a fertiliser factory in decline and some of the fine people taken down with it.

I asked John to read this, to see if he wanted to change anything. He refused to even look at it.

'I trust you, doll,' he said.

Doll?

OK, then. Gloves off. Carte blanche.

One

Demolition

The demolition crew found the body.

A gale blew across Leith docks, drowning the rumble of bulldozers, squeal of hydraulic scissors, juddering percussion of jackhammers and crash of falling masonry. Gusts of wind whipped the concrete dust into weird shapes: mini tornadoes with tentacles and claws, ephemeral and monstrous.

The abandoned SAI fertiliser factory occupied a promontory of land reclaimed from the Firth of Forth, a fenced site that stretched two miles east–west and half a mile north–south on the edge of the Port of Leith, Edinburgh's dockland. Little remained above ground. The offices and stores, tanks and reactors, towers and chimneys had been reduced to shards of broken brick, jagged concrete wedges, spaghetti junctions of metal pipe and beam. The demolition forces, a phalanx of specialised destruction machines, trundled towards the last remaining structures above the deep-water dock. The mechanised locusts munched through the factory, flattening everything in their wake, leaving behind a wind-blown desert: order to chaos, symmetry to entropy, meaning to insignificance.

Kelly was driving the grapple, a hydraulic excavator with an articulated jaw in place of a digging bucket. Steel teeth chomped through the covered aerial conveyors which had once transported powdered phosphate rock on huge rubber belts to the heart of the factory. The grapple left a trail of carnage to be sorted and shifted.

From inside the 'hoose', a cab on a rotating platform above the moving undercarriage, Kelly manoeuvred the grapple gingerly towards the edge of the quay, alert to the sharp smell of seaweed. One false move and the bright yellow juggernaut with its crawler feet and long giraffe neck would topple into the North Sea. Even if he escaped from the hoose, the freezing water would kill him before they could fish him out of the shipping channel. Journey's end.

Kelly attacked the final structure, an elevator tower designed to raise the ship's cargo from quay to conveyor. *Rat-a-tat-a-tat-rat-a-whoofffFFFF*. The walls of the intake elevator collapsed under Kelly's assault and a cloud of rose-gold confetti mushroomed and shimmered above the ruin. As the dust cleared, he edged forward, peering through the grimy glass of the cab at the exposed elevator shaft, grapple poised, one hand on the joystick, ready to rip its guts out.

Something stayed his hand. He couldn't say exactly what. A lull in the wind? A break in the clouds? The plaintive cry of a gull that sounded almost human? A shaft of sunlight illuminated shapes beneath the metal structure. Scratching his head, Kelly flicked the windscreen wipers to nashing and matched the stroke with a squealing rag on the inside of the glass. He peered through, swallowed hard, and stopped the machine.

Angry Pat responded to the radio call, stomping over the rubble, bellowing obscenities. The demolition crew foreman followed the new yodelling school of management. What started out as a quiet transaction in a warm office, a contract signed with just the scratch of a biro on smooth paper, was amplified over time into a series of increasingly strident shouting matches. Angry Pat was the last in the line of yodellers. Having received his instructions over mountains of obstacles, across gulleys of incomprehension, he passed them on by haranguing with ever-increasing ferocity and volume, berating men who valued their jobs too much to shout back.

Kelly ignored the tirade, as he ignored most of the invective that spewed from Angry Pat, and nodded at the ruined tower. Crumbs of concrete dangled on threads of steel reinforcement bars. The elevator, a tangle of buckets and chains, was listing to one side, the flimsy floor had been torn apart to reveal the machine room below. A metal ladder led down past a huge pulley wheel into a deep basement. Directly underneath the wheel, a conical mound of powdered rock had formed, undisturbed for years, most likely, but now slowly collapsing, like a sandcastle at high tide. With a grimy finger, Kelly pointed to the unmistakable shape of a human head which had emerged from the settling pile.

'Jesus Christ!' Angry Pat backed away, eyes wide.

The job had a tight schedule. The old fertiliser factory on the docks had to be razed to the ground before the area could be redeveloped as a shopping and entertainment centre. It was a fixed-price demolition contract and they were already over budget. Angry Pat hesitated, looking sideways at Kelly with an unspoken request. Kelly turned away and spat into the sea.

The foreman's shoulders slumped. 'Virgin Mary's bollocks.'

He phoned his boss before he called the police.

It took days to sift through the rubble. The police impounded the demolition equipment, machines too crude for delicate excavation. The crew were laid off; no other jobs would take lone men who were only as useful as the snippers and dozers and grapples they operated. Kelly remained on half wages to hang around and guard the kit.

New machines arrived: tiny grabbers and sifters, with hoses and sniffer snouts, followed by men and women in white overalls with brushes and bags who took care not to disturb the body, hand-digging to preserve as much evidence as possible.

Kelly made it a rule to stay well clear of the police, but the woman in uniform tracked him down to the store where he took naps between security shifts.

'Detective Inspector Rose Irvine.' She announced herself with a rap on the door of the windowless lock-up. 'Can I have a word?'

He rubbed the sleep from his eyes and ran fingers though tousled hair, catching an unpleasant whiff of his own oxters.

She waited for him to emerge and lock the door before she marched back to the crime scene. He stopped to take a leak behind one of the huge rubber tyres, zipped himself up and followed.

'You the lad that found... this?' She nodded towards the vault where a police photographer was fiddling with his camera.

'Aye.'

He paused at the lip of the crater. A vacuum truck had sucked away the last of the powdered rock, and Kelly let out a gasp as he took in the scene below.

Everything in the basement under the elevator pulley was encased by a thin shell of hardened phosphate rock, creating a macabre tableau. The human figure could be seen clearly now, seated on a chair, the body upright, hands resting on a rude desk, fingers splayed as if pointing to several objects on the flat surface. The head, the body, the furniture and the objects, perfectly preserved.

'Tell me exactly what happened.'

'I already told the polis—'

'Tell *me*.'

He reappraised her. Not one to mess with, for all she looked like a wee clootie dumpling. But there was little enough to tell. He translated the technical terms of demolition into lassie-speak as best he could.

'Looks almost staged,' she said.

He shook his head. 'Whoever it was, they lived there.'

'How do you know?'

Kelly pointed to the braziers. On either side of the seated figure stood two perforated 50-gallon drums, the tops hacked off to leave jagged steel edges, multiple saucer-sized holes punched through the sides. The sort of luxury item working men rely on for heat during winter jobs.

'Who is it? How did this happen? Any ideas?'

Kelly shook his head. He had no clue, but he knew one person who might. A man who knew everything that ever went on in the old factory.

'You'd best talk to John.'

Two

John

John has a face like a well-kept grave.

He arrives early one morning at Torphichen Street Police Station: a tall, thin man with cropped grey hair and the demeanour of a professional undertaker. He is neatly dressed in polished leather shoes, grey trousers with stay-press seam, an ironed white shirt, blue tie and burgundy V-neck jumper under a padded anorak. Despite the layers, he shivers in the slanting winter light and blinks repeatedly as he states his business at the counter.

'I've come about the ess-eh-eye.'

A short, plump woman emerges from a side room with outstretched hand. She wears a black serge uniform with silver buttons and epaulettes, fair hair scraped back from a round face.

'Mr. Gibson?'

She smells of flowers and reminds him of summer.

'Aye.'

'Detective Inspector Rose Irvine.' Her handshake is warm and surprisingly firm. 'Thanks for coming in.'

He follows her up a flight of steps and waits while she recovers her breath. Outside Interview Room Number Two she gestures for him to enter, but he holds the door open so she can go in first.

The room is furnished with a wooden table and four metal chairs, the furniture marooned on a sea of blue linoleum, adrift between plain grey walls under a high barred window and a ticking clock. On the table is a manila folder.

'You worked at the SAI?' she asks. 'Scottish Agricultural Industries?'

'Aye.'

'We found a body in the old Leith works.'

John places his hands flat against the table, leaning onto it for support.

'Sit,' she says. 'Please.'

His complexion has paled from ivory to ash, his breathing is fast and ragged. She observes him closely as he sinks onto the chair.

When he raises his eyes again, they are wide with shock. 'Who is it?'

'We don't know yet,' she says.

'Poor beggar.'

She leans forward. 'Any idea why there might be a dead body in your old factory?'

'No.' He shakes his head.

'Until I get the autopsy results, I don't know the date of death, the cause of death, whether the victim was male or female, young or old, tall or short, fat or thin.' She sits back and stretches her hands out, palms upwards. She has nice hands, capable hands. 'Can you help me?'

'I can try.'

She opens the folder and shows John the photographs. 'What can you tell me?'

His shiver turns to a shudder. 'Poor beggar died before 1997.'

'Why do you say that?'

John wrinkles his brow. 'Production stopped.'

'I see.'

'And after 1955,' he adds.

'When production started?' She frowns. 'A forty-two-year window?'

He nods.

His working life.

First Clue

THE EBONY ELEPHANT

SULPHUR

Three

The Ebony Elephant

Inside the interview room of Torphichen Street Police Station, Rose is the first to break the silence.

'Can you identify the items found beside the body, the things on the desk?' She extracts a photograph from the manila folder and hands it to John. 'Here's a close-up.'

He takes off his glasses and brings the print to the end of his nose.

'We cleaned the objects up,' she says. 'Do you want to see them?'

'Aye.'

She picks up the phone and punches a number. 'Bring in the SAI evidence.'

Please, he thinks to himself.

'To Interview Room Two,' she says. 'Right away.'

Thanks, he adds silently as she puts down the phone. After all, it doesn't cost anything.

At a knock on the door, he is first on his feet, opening the door for a young constable who carries a metal tray.

Rose nods at the table, and the constable rests the tray carefully on the near edge.

John moves the stack of photographs to one side so she can slide it into the centre.

'Thank you,' she smiles.

'You're welcome,' he says.

Rose waves the constable away.

John sits again. He stares at each of the objects for exactly ninety seconds, one after the other, then closes his eyes.

Rose waits.

The clock ticks.

Rose waits some more.

When he opens his eyes, she leans forward. 'Any ideas?'

'Can I touch them?'

She nods.

John picks up a little ebony elephant, about the size of his fist, tail curved, trunk down, ears alert, expertly carved. He strokes the smooth wood. One sharp white tusk is loose. John pulls it out, brings first the matchstick-sized shard, and then the empty socket, to his nose. He sniffs. Once. Twice. He pulls away and licks his lips, wrinkles his nose then bends forward and inhales again. Thrice.

Yes, there it is. No doubt about it. Just a trace, a whiff, but unmistakable.

Sulphur.

Four

Sulphur

Sulphur formed deep in massive stars when helium and silicon reacted at temperatures of two and a half billion degrees centigrade before flying through space in dust, asteroids and planetesimals, to become the fifth most abundant element on earth.

Take a hair from your head. Poke it into the flame of a candle. Sniff the singed end. That smell comes from sulphur, an essential part of the protein that makes up our muscles. An adult human body contains over two hundred grams of sulphur[1].

Pure sulphur melts just above the boiling point of water. The yellow solid turns dark red as it liquefies, burning with a blue flame as it spews out of volcanoes.

Much of the sulphur on planet earth is chemically bound to other elements in stable compounds.

The metal sulphides form colourful crystals: with iron to form golden pyrite[2], the fools' gold that tricked many a hapless miner; with mercury to give vermillion cinnabar[3] – a toxic Roman rouge; with lead to give galena[4], with antimony to give stibnite[5] – the original kohl eyeliner and mascara, and with zinc to give sphalerite[6] gems shining with a dark, adamantine lustre.

The sulphate minerals include gypsum[7], the original plaster of Paris; alunite[8], a flocculant used to clarify turbid liquids; and barite[9], used in oil and gas exploration as a heavy drilling mud.

'Free' elemental sulphur is also found in nature. It forms the crust around hot springs, lurks under salt domes and skulks under mountains, sinuous crystalline tendrils stretching across the island of Sicily.

For as long as written records exist, sulphur has been used for medicine and fumigation, to bleach cloth and wage war. It may have been a component of the ancient liquid weapon called Greek fire, and it is certainly a component in gunpowder, invented in ninth-century China.

Sulphur was first recognised as a chemical element by Antoine Lavoisier[vi] in 1777, but his brilliance as a scientist didn't save him from the French revolution. Seventeen years later he lost his head to the guillotine.

A different upheaval, the industrial revolution, led to an increase in demand for sulphur, leading to a rapid expansion of the mines in Sicily, opening one of the most barbaric chapters of modern times.

Life must have been hard indeed for a Sicilian family to consider sending a child to the sulphur mines. In return for a payment, the *soccorso morto*, a father handed over his six-year-old son to live and work in a distant mine, indentured to a stranger for the next ten years. If the child survived that long.

Did they know what they were selling their children into? The sulphur miners worked underground, stripped bare. While a man, a *picconiero*, hacked at the sulphur with a pickaxe, the job of his boy, a *caruso*, was to crawl through narrow tunnels, barefoot, in total darkness, and haul the material to the surface. The loads varied between twenty kilograms for the youngest and seventy kilograms for the older boys. The smaller the load, the more frequent the hellish journey. Temperatures underground reached forty-five degrees centigrade with humidity at 100 per cent, the air thick with rock dust and choking, noxious gases. The fatality rate was high. Mine workers were incinerated in underground fires and explosions, buried alive by rock falls and collapsing tunnels, drowned when the manual mine pumps failed to keep up with the rising water, or simply suffocated in the foul miasma of unventilated tunnels.

The boys were beaten and burnt to encourage compliance. Their growth was stunted, their little bodies deformed by the punishing work, and the hell continued above ground.

The sulphur had to be freed from the rock it clung to. In fuel- and water-poor Sicily, the sulphur itself became the fuel. Ore was piled into an inclined ditch and set alight. As the sulphur burned, the temperature inside the pile increased, and molten sulphur flowed out. In this primitive *calcarella* (and later *calcaroni*) method, over half the sulphur was lost, much of it as choking, toxic sulphur dioxide gas which polluted the air and blackened vegetation for miles around.

In this infernal landscape, the boys slept with their masters in primitive huts or in the open air; even at night, there was no escape. Those *carusi* who survived to the age of sixteen became miners themselves and repeated the cycle of enslavement and abuse[10].

Brutality breeds brutality. After a terrible drought in 1893, men organised themselves to fight for better working conditions through a new socialist movement, the *Fasci Siciliani dei Lavoratori*. The Italian government refused to send troops to repress the workers, so the wealthy Sicilian landowners turned elsewhere for protection: to a new private army – the Mafia.

Booker T. Washington[xx], himself a former slave, reported in 1910, '…a sulphur mine in Sicily is about the nearest thing to hell that I expect to see in this life… These boy slaves were frequently beaten and pinched, in order to wring from their overburdened bodies the last drop of strength they had in them. When beatings did not suffice, it was the custom to singe the calves of their legs with lanterns to put them again on their feet. If they sought to escape from this slavery in flight, they were captured and beaten, sometimes even killed.'[11]

Why was sulphur suddenly so important?

The sulphur hauled up from the subterranean mines of Sicily was mainly used to manufacture sulphuric acid, which went into the production of soap, medicines, dyestuffs, glass, textiles, paper, fertiliser and explosives. From 1801 to 1907, annual production of sulphuric acid rose from four thousand to over a million tonnes in the UK alone.

Alternative ways to obtain sulphur, that didn't involve enslaving and crippling children, came from the application of science and technology. When sulphur was discovered in Louisiana, USA, those attempting to access it from the surface drowned in quicksand. In 1894, the German-born chemist Herman Frasch[xviii], later dubbed the king of sulphur, came up with a better solution. He injected superheated water into the underground deposit with one metal 'straw' and sucked out the molten sulphur with another. Aerating the liquid sulphur to make it float on the water made the process even more reliable. Brain beats brawn, every time.

It was the abundance of oil in nearby Texas, replacing wood or coal to heat the water, that made the elegant Frasch process economic, driving extraction costs down to a fifth of those at the Caltanissetta mine in Sicily.

Oil provided not only the energy needed to replace Sicilian child muscle, but brought, inside itself, a new source of sulphur. Oil is formed from plants and animals that lived and died and were buried under new life growing so fast that the residue was starved of oxygen. As ancient living matter decomposed under unusual conditions of temperature and pressure, anaerobic bacteria transformed it into hydro-carbons: coal, oil and gas.

Sulphur is essential for life, incorporated into amino acids which form proteins. As ancient living matter decays it leaves a residue of complex organo-sulphur compounds.

The residual sulphur is a major problem in oil extraction and refining. Not only does it smell terrible, but it corrodes metal and causes atmospheric pollution as it is released.

Above 0.5 per cent sulphur, the crude oil is classed as 'sour' and has to be 'stabilised' to leave a 'sweet' crude. In modern refineries, hydrogen is bubbled though the oil over a catalyst of cobalt and molybdenum, extracting the sulphur in the form of hydrogen sulphide, a toxic gas with the aroma of rotten eggs.

The easiest way to deal with the stinky gas is to turn it back into elemental sulphur. Fortunately, there is an elegantly simple way to do so: the Claus process.

Carl Friedrich Claus[xvii] was a German-born chemist, living and working in England when in 1893 he patented his process to recover solid sulphur.

In the first phase of the Claus process[A], the hydrogen sulphide gas is fed to a furnace and burnt with a restricted amount of air so that only one third of it is oxidised, to form sulphur dioxide. The sulphur dioxide and remaining hydrogen sulphide continue over a catalyst bed of titanium dioxide and react to form sulphur and water.

As oil production increased, so did the clean production of pure sulphur from oil. The Sicilian mines became uneconomic and closed. Millions of Sicilians emigrated to America to start a new life.

Five

A Ruptured Hose

It was during the unloading of the *Eylenya* – a ship later beached at Chittagong and broken up for scrap by Bangladeshi workers – when the incident happened.

The *Eylenya* was one of the fast boats that sailed from Holland, bringing sulphur straight from the petrochemical refineries of Rotterdam. The skipper of the *Eylenya*, Captain Jan Bosma, a phlegmatic native of Middelburg in Zeeland, was a regular visitor to Edinburgh.

Inside the ship's hold, the flakes gleamed bright yellow and smelt bad. Sometimes the sulphur caked and set solid in huge slabs that had to be broken up by hand. The stevedores, responsible for offloading raw materials at Leith docks, loathed sulphur. The slightest friction set it on fire and the stench of the gas made them puke – sulphur monoxide, sulphur dioxide, sulphur trioxide – choking and deadly.

Before the stevedores could start offloading, a factory representative boarded the ship to inspect the manifest – the cargo – and agree the offloading plan. Ship crews used to the efficiency of Singapore or Rotterdam were surprised by Leith docks. The stevedores operated only during daylight hours, with prolonged breaks for breakfast, dinner and tea. For some seamen it made a welcome change from arriving and unloading on the same day. The crew could disembark, walk up Constitution Street and catch a bus to the centre of

Edinburgh and the glories of the old town looming over the new. New in 1830 that is.

John always volunteered to carry out the inspection if he was on shift when the ship arrived. He befriended many of the captains over the years. They brought him small gifts, and he hoarded these trinkets in a large cupboard set aside for the purpose, waiting for an opportunity to distribute a miniature bottle of schnapps, a leather strap or a woven bangle to a particularly deserving team member.

Once the cargo was accepted and the loading plan agreed, the Leith stevedores scaled one-hundred-foot ladders and settled down in the cabs of two huge cranes. Working in tandem to a precise, if unwritten, choreography, they took turns to lower the grab buckets into the ship's hold, lifting the flakes, and depositing the yellow brimstone into open-topped lorries that sped to the entrance of the fertiliser factory half a mile away. Streamers of yellow dust fanned through the teeth of the buckets, occasionally catching fire. Ribbons of blue flame sparkled and crackled against platinum skies. When a sulphur boat came in, John always requested an extra man from the factory day crew to stand ready to extinguish the sulphur fires with seawater from a red rubber hose.

Inside the factory, John managed his shift team with an iron fist, assigning tasks and tracking performance with military precision, but the two day teams were controlled by others.

The maintenance crew of welders, riggers, turners, tiffys, sparkies, carpenters, mechanics and fitters were ably managed by Roderick, an energetic marine engineer who responded to dry land with perpetual motion. He paced the miles of factory road, from dockside to ammonia spheres, from sulphur melters to Nitram packing, from workshop to store, a lightning flash of white hair and wisdom.

The services crew managed themselves, contrary to the belief of the blustering, ineffectual university graduate who imagined that workmen could be led from the comfort of an office, and provided the manual labour according to a strict hierarchy. At the top sat the wannabe craftsmen, those who didn't make the grade for a full apprenticeship but could drive a forklift truck and speak the lingo. Tolerated as craft assistants, they carried tools, fetched spares, sorted scrap and brought extra muscle, elbow grease or welly as required. In the middle lay those who unloaded the raw materials or packed the product. At the bottom skulked the greasers.

A fertiliser factory hums with moving parts. As one surface rubs against another it causes friction and wear. Regular adjustment and lubrication prevent breakdown. Gearboxes must be topped up with oil, rotating shafts greased with a thick lard-like jelly, packing injected from the nozzle of a special gun. The greasers performed these vital factory tasks, and not just lubrication, but machinery attendance. The same person laid hands on the same machine every few days. They felt compressors running hot, heard pumps squealing, smelt burning rubber from slipping drive belts, saw unwelcome flecks of shiny metal glittering in oil sumps. Expert – if unconscious – tribologists, they might be unaware of Stribeck curves and elastohydrodynamic rheology, but the maintenance manager, Roderick, relied on them totally. Not just for lubrication, but for condition monitoring, early warning of impending failure. Despite the pivotal importance of the role, tradition dictated that the job of greaser went to the humblest man.

The three greasers were, each in their own way, a couple of

sandwiches short of a picnic. Fat Willy had probably eaten all of his, along with many deep-fried suppers washed down with pints of heavy. His curly hair and ruddy face waggled atop a spherical body propelled by short legs that lumbered from job to job. He entertained colleagues with musical farts and half-remembered dirty jokes. The punchlines were often delivered at the last minute by Smart Sandy.

Fat Willy's sidekick was the same height but a quarter the girth, a dour bald man wearing a permanent scowl that belied an uncomplaining, obliging nature.

Smart Sandy (named ironically) followed Fat Willy's instructions without question, scaling giant ladders and limbo-dancing under pipes, sometimes to reach a grease nipple, sometimes just for the entertainment of others, oblivious to the laughs and jeers that rewarded his puppet-like antics and ventriloquist dummy one-liners. The first two kept their distance from the third member of the grease team. Becksy usually worked alone. Perhaps from preference, but he smelt so bad on Monday mornings that no one really cared to find out. Even if they had wished to ask, the profoundly deaf man could neither read nor write and his version of sign language was not understood in Leith. Nevertheless, when it came to preventative maintenance, Becksy was the smartest of the crew.

One February morning Fat Willy had been summoned from normal duties to stand fire watch for the *Eylenya*, leaving Smart Sandy to complete his lubrication round alone. Grumbling and chuntering at the inconvenience, Fat Willy connected a fire hose to the first hydrant he came across and stretched the long red snake across the roadway that connected the dock to the plant. He opened the valve and propped up a couple of old crates to sit on. He was settling down in the winter sunshine, when John came running towards him, arms flailing like windmills.

Too late.

The lorries moved faster than John. The drivers didn't even notice the red hose as they drove over it. *Duh-duum, duh-duum, duh-duum, duh-dumm.* Eight sets of wheels compressed and released the hose in two places, six feet apart, each pair of steel-reinforced tyres stretching and pinching, warping and snagging, scraping and dragging against the gravel. One lorry and then another drove forward as they lined up to receive the sulphur.

John arrived in time to halt the third lorry. He bent to inspect the hose just as it sprang a leak. A spray of ice-cold seawater hit him full in the face.

Fat Willy remained frozen beside the hydrant until Captain Jan Bosma barked at him to stop the flow. His palms sweated against the wheel of the sea-water valve, slipping and sliding as he struggled to turn it clockwise, but gradually the height of the fountain diminished, and John appeared through the spray, soaked from head to toe.

'Catch!' The captain threw a towel from the ship. The greaser grabbed it and waddled towards John, arms outstretched, his face sweetened by a nervous smile.

John rarely smiled. He was sensitive about his teeth. The effort to keep his mouth closed, coupled with a reflex which jerked his hand up to cover it, kept his emotions hidden. The skin wrinkling briefly around narrowed eyes was the only clue.

His laugh, on the other hand, could not be missed. It was Halloween. His long thin body went into spasms, twitching and gyrating as deep bellows developed into a series of high-pitched shrieks. It went on too long. People were rightly afraid of John's laugh. The master of sarcasm, John managed to make an outbreak of mirth indicate just the reverse. He used it to warn, to belittle, to chastise, to punish. No words were necessary. A prolonged manic laugh from John was enough to elicit complete surrender, abject capitulation from the subject of his attentions, a breast-beating *mea culpa*, a sincere apology, a genuine resolution not to let him down again.

John turned his weaponised laugh on Fat Willy, decreasing the distance between their noses, trembling with vibrato, stretching the rubato, increasing the pitch and volume, until the greaser dropped his eyes in sulky apology.

John ordered him to roll up the damaged hose and carry it, by himself, one hundred yards away and hook it up to the correct hydrant. Confused, Fat Willy obeyed. Satisfied that his point was made, John instructed him to disconnect it and carry it one hundred yards back to where he started, and then a further five hundred yards to the workshop for repair. He radioed for the storeman to find Becksy, a greaser he could trust, and send him down with a new fire hose and a set of dry clothes.

The ship's captain lent John his cabin, along with a nip from his hip flask.

When John emerged in dry overalls, the stevedores observed from the cranes as the fire-fighting precautions were reinstated by Becksy and minutely inspected by John. They waited until the moment he gave the go-ahead to resume operations before calling a halt for break time and downing tools. Captain Jan Bosma telexed the shipping line to inform them that the *Eylenya* would be an extra day in port.

Captain Bosma took advantage of the extra time in

Edinburgh to attend the opening of an exhibition by modernist artist Dan Flavin[xxv], at the Modern Art Galleries in the Botanic Gardens. He responded so enthusiastically to the soothing artistic effect of coloured neon lights in empty white rooms that he decided to declutter his own cabin.

It snowed overnight. A fine dusting of pure white settled over the *Eyleyna*, its yellow cargo, the tall rust-red cranes, the blue seawater hydrant and the grey concrete dock. The morning sun burned though the haar as John's boots crunched across sparkling snow, a vast expanse of white marked only by the quatrefoils of birds' feet and the diamond tracks of an intrepid fox.

'*Goedemorgen*!' Captain Jan Bosma was already on deck. A tall man, even for a Zeelander raised on herring and milk, he stretched his spine, hands behind his head, surveying the clean white empty dock. If he was dismayed at the lack of activity, he was polite enough not to comment.

John nodded at the silent cranes. 'Stevies are meeting now. They won't restart until the snow's away.' He grimaced. 'Maybe the morrow.'

The captain offered John a mug of coffee and they stood side by side, one on the ship, one on the dock, and sipped the hot, bitter liquid. It tasted better, richer, in the snow. The captain nodded at the neatly coiled hose, now frosted with diamonds. 'You fully recovered from your soaking?'

'I'll live,' John replied. 'How was your exhibition?'

The captain beamed and described the regenerative effect of minimalism in glowing terms before adding, 'I have something for you.'

He held out the ebony elephant, picked up in Colombo and now, after the decluttering, surplus to decorative requirements. As John reached across the ship's rail to exchange an empty coffee mug for the carved gift, one of the little tusks fell through the snow into the sulphur below. The captain retrieved the wooden peg, brushed it down and handed it to John with the words of Cicero: *Omnium rerum principia parva sunt.*

Everything has a small beginning.

Further snowfall kept the ship in dock. The owners were not amused as they counted the costs of delay. They never made the mistake a second time.

The price of importing sulphur rose.

The first nail in the factory coffin.

John visited the exhibition *'monument' for V. Tatlin* by the minimalist artist Dan Flavin on his next day off.

Although entry was free, he felt cheated.

One. Two. Three. Four. Five. John counts the tiny ridges as he runs his left pinkie across the trunk of the little elephant. Water from an elephant's trunk. Water from hoses. John knows where the elephant came from and when.

'1975,' he says and looks up at Detective Inspector Rose Irvine.

Her eyes flash. The eyelashes are almost white, only the blue tips where she has applied mascara are defined. She waits.

'Jan Bosma,' he says. 'Captain of the *Eylenya*, a sulphur boat, brought this to Leith docks.'

She writes something down. She is left-handed and uses her right hand to shield her notes from view. The cuticles are ragged, zigzagging around the base of short, irregular fingernails. She must bite them.

'February 1975.'

'How can you be so sure of the date?'

'It snowed. I saw a daft wee exhibition of funny lights.'

She nods at the photograph of the mummified body. 'Is this Captain Jan Bosma?'

'No.' John shakes his head. 'He's still sailing.'

The detective wrinkles her nose; the small pink triangle turns up at the tip. She sighs. Why is she disappointed? Surely narrowing down the date of death from a forty-two-year window to half of that is progress?

'If a ship's captain gave you the elephant,' she narrows her eyes, 'then how did it come to end up in the phosphate cave?'

'I gave it away,' John said.

She leans forward. 'Who to?'

John places the ebony carving on the table and sits back. He closes his eyes. An elephant never forgets. Nor can John, but he isn't ready to talk about Blind Willy.

Not yet.

Second Clue

THE SILVER BULLET
PHOSPHATE ROCK

Six

Silver Bullet

In the police interview room, a telephone rings. *Brrring*. An old-fashioned bell, it echoes round the bare room. Detective Inspector Rose Irvine answers.

'Yes?' she barks and then frowns. 'Yes, sir. Right away, sir.'

She puts down the receiver and checks her watch.

'We'll break for lunch,' she says.

John steps out to breathe.

He marches east to Lothian Road, dropping behind St Cuthbert's into Princes Street Gardens where the path curves in the lee of the castle. Traversing the Mound, past Waverley Station, he looks up at the big clock over the North British Hotel and adjusts his watch as the One o'Clock Gun fires. Ignoring the pain from his arthritic hip, he continues to the top of the Carlton Hill where Edinburgh unfolds before him: the Pentland Hills to the south, the Ochils to the north, and the silvery Firth of Forth snaking through a broad valley in-between.

The only ship in Leith docks now is the Royal Yacht Britannia on a permanent mooring. No cargo boats. He narrows his eyes to try and make out the remains of a factory.

For decades, John monitored production from the top of Leith Walk. He knew in advance what sort of shift to expect, making an accurate assessment by the colours in the sky. A thin streak of orange reassured him that the nitric acid plant was producing aqua fortis, a blue/grey haze above the Nitram tower told him that little white prills were rattling down inside, and the height of white steam soaring in puffy clouds from the tallest chimney gave the rate of granulation.

He always arrived early for the shift handover, walking round the plants before his own crew clocked on. He made sure that no one from the retiring mob disappeared for an early shower or left their logbook incomplete. Then he waited at the gatehouse for his morning or evening 'kiss'. As each arriving worker came towards the bars of the turnstile, John pressed his gaunt face against the other side and barred entry until they gave him a whiff of their breath. Those with nothing to hide endured the ritual without complaint. Others, men still recovering from a bad pint or who had taken a whisky breakfast with the stevedores, might dissemble or protest. His long bony fingers would reach out, pinch a nose through the bars of the cage until they opened their lips. They either breathed onto his nose or backed away to call in 'sick'.

John possessed a finely tuned chromatograph in his nostrils. He could perfectly calibrate and overlook a single evening pint before night shift, although he was less forgiving about morning spirits. He encouraged the progress of the recovering alcoholics, monitoring the pungency of sweet ketosis, berating them when they fell off the wagon. Bad oral hygiene, a love of garlic, even super-strong Trebor mints did not interfere with the accurate assessment of blood alcohol level.

John took his first cup of tea standing at the window to keep an eye on the departing shift. He then walked round again to instruct each member of his own crew individually. Although John scanned the shift logs (hardbacked, narrow-lined books,

34

black with red spines) and glanced at the numbers scrawled onto pre-printed A3 sheets, he worked mainly by intuition: the opacity of the yellow haze over the sulphur melter, the taste of acid in the vacuum ejector hot wells, the thickness of ice on the spheres, the texture of warm fertiliser granules as he ran them through his hands, the pitch of the whistle from steam billowing into the sky.

Once things were settled and he had personally instructed each team member on what he expected of them, he returned to his office. On day shifts, he walked to the canteen, arriving just as it opened. On nights, John sat alone at his desk and ate two white bread and marmite sandwiches followed by the second of twelve cups of tea. The only concession to the unnatural working pattern was a Tunnock's caramel wafer at two in the morning when his body clock was screaming for sleep.

Today the air is clear. Wispy white clouds snake across a pale blue sky. From Carlton Hill, John gazes down over Edinburgh, following the road to Leith. Nothing remains of the tall factory structures. The demolition crew flattened everything above ground before they started excavating.

How can a complex manufacturing plant, once the lifeblood of Scottish agriculture, decades in construction, disappear in a matter of days?

John turns away with lead in his heart. The physical structures are gone, but what of the stories? The close-knit community? The livelihoods of a ragbag of assorted men?

And a few women.

John takes the bus back to Torphichen Street and limps into the interview room. Detective Inspector Rose Irvine is waiting for him. Her morning scent of roses is now mixed with a hint of caramelised tomato and roasted onion.

'Pizza for lunch?' John asks.

She nods and checks her white shirt for telltale traces, frowning up at him when she finds none. 'Ready to continue?'

'Aye.'

He inhales deeply before picking up the next object: a silver necklace. The pendant is barely recognisable as a bullet; the base has splattered into the petals of a flower. The links of the fine silver chain spill through his fingers as he hands it to the detective inspector.

She takes it and holds it up to the light. 'Do you recognise this?'

'Aye.'

'And?'

'It's from Jordan,' he says.

'A person or a place?'

He frowns. 'The Hashemite Kingdom of Jordan.'

'In the Middle East?'

'Aye.'

'So how did it get to Scotland?'

'In a cargo of phosphate rock.'

'And who did it belong to?'

In the police interview room, John turns to the window, feigning interest in a flock of birds swooping past, and remembers Polly.

Seven

Guano

Elemental phosphorus, nicknamed the devil's element, is highly flammable and will spontaneously combust in air. First isolated in 1669 by Hennig Brand[(iv)], it is named from the Greek *phosphorus mirabilis*, meaning miraculous bearer of light. Brand was a German alchemist looking for gold in urine (as one does). He discovered instead that, if you boil down twenty litres of urine, you can get one gram of this strange, volatile substance that glows in the dark and burns with a cold radiance.

Phosphorus makes matches, fireworks and incendiary bombs sparkle. It's also highly toxic – used in rat poison, herbicides, insecticides, chemical warfare and other forms of murder. However, once phosphorus is combined with oxygen and converted to phosphate, it becomes stable, non-toxic and has the power to regulate all life on earth.

The average human body contains over three kilograms[1] of phosphates, most of it in your bones as crystalline hydroxyapatite[12]. The hard, dense enamel of your teeth is formed from another phosphate, fluorapatite[13]. Every single cell in your body carries your genetic code, and the backbone of each strand of DNA[14] or RNA[15] is made from alternating phosphate and sugar groups. Inside the mitochondria, the powerhouses of the cell, another phosphate compound, ATP[16], regulates the energy flows in our body, with one of the triple phosphates breaking bonds to release energy, leaving a double phosphate (ADP[17]) behind. The energy from food is used to regenerate the phosphate–phosphate bonds and the human body recycles its own weight in ATP every day.

Some phosphates in your body are excreted, in urine and faeces, and need to be constantly replenished. There is no phosphate in the air you breathe, very little in the water you drink, and so you ingest it with your food. Animals get phosphate from the plants they eat, and plants get phosphates from the soil.

Phosphorus helps plants 'fix' carbon dioxide from the air, as part of a series of reactions called the Calvin cycle. Using the energy from the sun, plants turn gaseous carbon dioxide into glucose and other sugars during photosynthesis with the help of the most abundant enzyme on earth: rubisco[18] a phosphorus-containing enzyme that acts as a catalyst during the first major step of carbon fixation[19]. Phosphorus regulates the energy which sustains life.

But there's a constant need to replenish this element. Very little phosphorus is recycled. Apart from slaughterhouse products such as bonemeal, the concentrations are too low for practical recovery. Farm animals and crops take more phosphate out of the ground than they put back, so the balance must come from elsewhere.

In the middle of the ocean, an uninhabited island rises from the sea. The tip of an extinct volcano, its sheer cliffs plunge vertically to the crashing waves, but the rocky crater provides shelter and a resting place for migrating birds: cormorants, pelicans and boobies. The birds feed, sleep and fly on, leaving a little something behind.

Guano is the accumulated excrement of seabirds and bats. A Spanish corruption of the word 'wanu' from Quechua, an

38

indigenous language of the South American Andes, it originally referred to any form of dung used as an agricultural fertiliser.

In the harsh desert land that makes up much of Peru, indigenous people were already using guano to enrich the soil five thousand years before the Spanish arrived. The Inca emperors valued the precious material so highly that they restricted access to all but a few licenced collectors and punished disturbance of seabirds with death.

The Prussian explorer Alexander von Humboldt[viii] wrote about the incredible fertilising properties of guano in 1802. In 1813 English chemist Humphry Davy[x] highlighted the special efficacy of Peruvian guano in his book *Elements of Agricultural Chemistry*. The book became a bestseller, and so did guano.

In a canny move, the Peruvian government nationalised its guano resources and, in 1856, used the revenue to abolish slavery and free twenty-five-thousand slaves.

With prices rising, a search for new sources of guano began. Explorers targeted islands in dry regions, where the valuable nutrients left by seabirds remained *in situ*, instead of leaching out with every rain shower.

Ichaboe Island off the Diamond Coast of Namibia is one of the most densely packed and important breeding sites for seabirds. Safe from mainland predators, cormorants and penguins, gulls and oystercatchers, terns and gannets nest on the island. Each year, fifty thousand birds share the low-lying island. Over time, they built up guano deposits seven metres deep.

The demand for guano became so fierce – the *white gold* rush – it led to America's first imperialist experiment. In 1856, the Guano Islands Act was passed, encouraging American citizens to claim land for the United States.

Whenever any citizen of the United States discovers a deposit of guano on any island, rock, or key, not within the lawful jurisdiction of any other Government, and not occupied by the citizens of any other Government, and takes peaceable possession thereof, and occupies the same, such island, rock, or key may, at the discretion of the President, be considered as appertaining to the United States[20].

About one hundred guano-rich, uninhabited islands in the Caribbean and Pacific oceans were annexed by the USA. The labourers shipped in to extract the guano worked in terrible conditions. A quarter of a century after the abolition of slavery, little had changed and in 1889, the Navassa Island Rebellion led to the deaths of five white overseers. The trial of the black contract workers from Maryland went to the US Supreme Court, and death sentences were eventually commuted.

A new source of phosphate was required.

By the time John joined the fertiliser factory in Leith, phosphate rock arrived in slow boats from Africa. A fine golden powder mixed with small pebbles and the occasional bullet.

Eight

Ladies of Leith

When word got around that a phosphate boat was coming in from Dakar, the Ladies of Leith would congregate. They had learned not to bother with the Sulphur boats. Dutch officers sometimes brought their wives or friends but, even unencumbered, the Dutch sailors were cold and mean, preferring a walk in the Royal Botanic Garden, with its quirky sculpture collection, to a warm, fee-paying embrace. The boats from Senegal had lonely international crews with little interest in modern art.

If he was on shift the morning after the boat came in, John would go and meet the captain. He would make as much noise as possible on the gangplank, clattering and coughing, before knocking and waiting outside the cabin in case the captain still had company. Sometimes he met Polly leaving as he arrived, and they would exchange cordial greetings. Each had their job to do. John treated the Ladies of Leith with respect. If he disapproved of their profession, he didn't show it. He afforded them the same courtesy that he showed to any female. He was considerate, old-fashioned, broad-minded and a little intimidated.

If Polly had paid attention during school chemistry lessons, she might have remembered the importance of phosphate to our DNA. The other elements – carbon, oxygen, hydrogen, and to some extent (if you are leguminous) nitrogen – can be ingested from air and water, but phosphorus comes from the soil.

Seventy per cent of Polly's bones were made up of hydroxyapatite; her body contained three kilograms of calcium phosphate[1]. When she remembered to eat, she ingested about a gram of phosphorus each day.

Polly understood that phosphate was essential to her life. The money that she made on the boats allowed her to buy heroin.

The powdered phosphate rock didn't catch fire, unlike sulphur, so the stevedores used the Siwertell. This giant Archimedes' screw rotated inside a huge pipe attached to a dockside crane. It tunnelled into the soft mound of powder in the ship's hold. The powdered rock spiralled up the screw, rising five metres above the quay before falling into a small hopper which fed the bucket elevator. Forty buckets, connected by chains, rotated around four sprocket wheels, two in the machine room under the elevator shaft, the others at the top of the elevator. The buckets descended empty, scooped up powder as it fell from the quayside hopper and lifted it twenty metres, dumping it into a silo sitting wreathed in a golden mist high above the dock. From the silo, the powdered rock dropped through sieving screens onto a series of rubber conveyor belts that transported it two miles to the giant sheds at the back of the factory. Sheds with the profile of a whale's jawbone, a leviathan arch and span.

They said that the rock had no smell, but John could detect the heat of the Saharan sun in every golden particle.

The day of the explosion started with a perfect sunrise. The sky was still dark as John made his way down Leith Walk, but as he turned east through the dock gates the embryo sun was already turning the sky a deep blue.

The *Gardyloo* was on the move and John caught a nauseating whiff as it passed. Named after the Edinburgh warning cry as people emptied buckets of waste from high windows onto the street below, a corruption of the French *gardez l'eau* – look out for the water, with water here being used euphemistically – The *Gardyloo* continued that fine medieval tradition of dumping human waste. The shit ship filled up at an effluent station on the dock and took Edinburgh's sewage out to the deep ocean, taking all the excreted nitrate, potassium and phosphate salts with it.

The swing bridge opened to let the boat out, cutting off the shortest route to the factory. John cursed. If he'd arrived two minutes earlier, he'd be in his office by now. He began the long hike round the dock basin, surveying the chimneys and columns that soared up behind the bulk store. From left to right: a fine white mist from the top of the rectangular prilling tower meant the Nitram plant was operating. It was still too dark to see the wisps of orange from the tallest column, but the silver steel was just starting to glow, and steam rose from the cooling towers, so NAP3 was also on. A dense woolly stack curled up from SAP1. Was it starting up or shutting down? Not a wisp of steam from the next building along, or from the chimney at the end which meant that Supers and PAP must be off. But, joy of joys, a healthy white column, billowing upwards and inclining towards the sun, meant that the Granny was running at full rates. Wind south-westerly, blowing out to sea.

As he turned into the wind, toward the dock basin, he noticed that the overdue phosphate boat had finally arrived.

Phosphate rock for the Leith plant came from Senegal.

Most of the time. There were exceptions. Aberrations. Like the cargo on this boat beside the quay.

The heidjuns, men in head office, had been insistent that a change in supply from Senegal to Jordan would be seamless, but this first boat of Jordanian phosphate was already three weeks late. Judging by how low it sat in the water, offloading had only just begun. Not a good start. The PAP – phosphoric acid – and PhoSAI – superphosphate – plants had run out of feedstock and shut down, which meant that SAP1 – sulphuric acid – had to shut down too. The granulation plant might be running full tilt, but without feedstock, it was on borrowed time.

John rounded the bend and approached the factory gate. The gatehouse window opened at his approach and Alec raised a huge hand in salute. An ex-policeman, allegedly dismissed for brutality, he stood 6 feet 8 inches tall and weighed seventeen stone. He normally gave John no trouble, but everyone knew the gateman was best avoided with a drink inside him.

At the handover, the departing shift manager confirmed that the phosphate boat had started offloading without incident, so John took his time, doing his usual rounds and taking breakfast in the canteen before driving the works van down to Imperial Dock to check on progress.

As John approached the ship, he noticed the raised position of the gangplank, suggesting that the captain wasn't receiving visitors or, more probably, still had company.

He opened the door of the intake elevator shaft and descended the stairs. Becksy was already in the basement, up on a ladder attending to the pulley bearings, grease gun in hand.

John bent to where a pile of phosphate rock had spilt from

the elevator, a conical archive containing different strata from each cargo. The colour of the top layer, from the new Jordanian phosphate, was darker than the Senegalese layers below. He scooped a little from the base of the cone and let it run through his hands. The powdered rock was finer than normal, almost greasy to the touch, except for the little pieces of grit mixed in among the fine particles.

Whoosh...whip-crack!

John nearly jumped out of his skin at the sound of a muffled explosion. The vibrations from the top of the elevator startled Becksy so much he dropped the grease gun and hit the red mushroom-shaped button beside the pulley. The elevator groaned to a halt. John raced up the stairs. He found the bullet, still smoking, trapped in a sieving screen, amid pebbles and shells. He was used to finding cartridge cases, but it wasn't often that live ammunition survived the journey.

No serious damage was done: the bullet had torn through the side of one bucket, ricocheted off the structural steelwork of the elevator and fallen onto the oversize mesh above the rubber conveyor belt. He held the curious object gingerly, marvelling at the way a cold, hard instrument of death could be transformed into curves that were almost organic, splattered into something quite beautiful. He slipped it, still warm, into his pocket.

Exploding bullets in the Jordanian phosphate were the least of his problems.

A far more sinister time-bomb had started ticking.

Nine

Impurities

> I cannot overemphasise the importance of phosphorus not only to agriculture and soil conservation but also to the physical health and economic security of the people of the Nation. Many of our soil types are deficient in phosphorus, thus causing low yields and poor quality of crops and pastures[21].

Throughout the nineteenth century, the source of phosphate for fertiliser, along with nitrogen and potassium, was bird poo: guano. Millions of bird droppings found their way to Scottish farms.

International trade is not without risks. There is evidence that *Phytophthora infestans*, a virulent strain of potato blight, travelled with guano and seed potatoes from the Americas to Europe, initiating the Great Hunger. The potato famine caused death and deprivation in the Highlands and Islands, accelerating depopulation and emigration.

Ireland was hit hardest. A million Irish men, women and children starved to death between 1845 and 1852 and a million more emigrated, but still the guano trade accelerated, and demand began to outstrip supply.

As avian sources ran out, men turned to crustaceans for help.

The coast of North and West Africa once thronged with flagellating trilobites, ancient underwater cockroaches. Over time, the shallow seas receded, leaving an arachnomorph arthropod graveyard rich in phosphates. This sediment was mined and sold, but unlike bird poo, the phosphates in trilobite exoskeletons are bound in a lattice of insoluble chitin[22].

Spreading this directly on the fields, as had been done with guano, was a waste of the rich potential. The key ingredients needed to be digested, turned from an insoluble to a soluble form to release the phosphorus.

There are advantages to chemical processing: by exposing materials to high temperatures and strong acids, you destroy the moulds, bacteria and viruses that can be present in natural materials. *Phytophthora infestans* would not survive, but there are other impurities to contend with.

Inorganic impurities include traces of toxic heavy metals like cadmium, lead and arsenic or radioactive elements uranium and thorium, and organic impurities, such as mercaptans.

The name mercaptan comes from mercury capture, something they are very good at. Also called thiols, another portmanteau word[23], mercaptans are remarkable for their odours.

Some odours are pleasant. The aroma of roasting coffee comes from Furfuryl mercaptan[24] and grapefruit mercaptan[25] gives the citrus fruit its distinctive scent.

Others are disgusting.

The chemical weaponry employed by a skunk includes butane, methylbutane and quinolinemethane mercaptans. Humans detect skunk mercaptans at concentrations of ten parts per billion – a blade of grass in a football field, a single sheep in the whole of Wales – however owls and dogs can't smell thiols and continue to happily hunt the skunk. Just hope they don't bring one home.

Since the New London School disaster of 1937 when over three hundred people, mainly children, died after an undetected gas leak exploded during lessons, an odour is added to natural gas to make it easy to detect leaks.

The mercaptan of choice is tertiary butyl mercaptan[26]. Detectable at 0.3 parts per billion (a tick on the single sheep in Wales, a seed on the blade of grass in that football pitch) and by a strange twist of chemistry the very same substance formed by the reaction of sulphuric acid with tiny organic impurities in Jordanian phosphate rock.

Ten

Gas Leak

The first sign of trouble came from the other side of the railway tracks. The product from the granulation plant was packed in a long shed, half a mile from the factory, on Salamander Street, the main road connecting Newhaven to Portobello. The Sally Street packing crew bagged fertiliser in fifty-pound sacks and one-tonne bags. It was rough work for tough men.

Not long after the phosphoric acid plant had restarted on Jordanian phosphate, John received word from one of his many spies that the Sally shift had reported a gas leak and decamped to the pub. He jumped into the works van and drove over to save them from themselves. The men were entitled to a meal break like anyone else, and there was no rule that said it couldn't be a liquid meal in the Black Bull with go-go dancing entertainment. Being drunk at work, however, was a sackable offence and John's experience told him that most of the Sally shift wouldn't know when to stop. John intercepted Big Stu, Tommy and Ronnie in the street outside the pub and took them back to the packing line to begin the inquisition.

The men claimed it was unsafe to work with a gas leak. John pointed out that there was no gas supply anywhere near. But he had to agree with them that a strong smell of gas pervaded the long, low shed, and the street outside.

John phoned the British Gas Corporation hotline. The

emergency response team wearily confirmed that they had received hundreds of calls from North Edinburgh that evening but had been unable to find a single leak. They mentioned that they had already sent an emergency van to Salamander Street, tested for gas, and reassured the leading hand that it was safe to continue packing.

John berated Big Stu and laughed him and the rest of the team back to work. But John was concerned. Back in the factory, he walked round each of the production units. Nothing. He went back to the phosphoric acid plant, nose in the air, sniffing. It was barely detectable, but there was definitely something different. He made a full report to the factory management. They took no notice.

It happened again one week later. This time John took note of the wind direction, onshore; speed, low; temperature, mild. Exactly the same conditions as last time. No smell in the factory, but the stench hung heavy half a mile inland. John climbed on to the roof of the Salamander Street shed and looked across the railway sidings, over the bonded warehouses, the Albert dock and back to the factory. He raised his eyes to the chimney of the phosphoric acid plant, noting the inversion of the steam pouring out of the reactor chimney, how some wisps dipped and streamed inland, a blanket of noxious fog.

Polly was unconscious when the gas board arrived at her flat. The transient residents of the dilapidated concrete block in Granton did not constitute the most civic-minded community, but the smell of gas was so intense that they feared for their own safety. Had Polly finally done away with herself, her head in the gas oven? Thoughtless skanky bitch, to leave the gas on.

The British Gas Corporation engineer arrived and pointed out that the gas to Polly's council bedsit had been cut off many months ago for failure to pay her bill. At the sound of a child singing behind the locked door, he sought help. Police broke in to find a chubby toddler in a clean and sparkly fairy outfit stroking the rose-gold hair of her emaciated mother just as Polly started to fit from the fentanyl-laced heroin her dealer was testing. An ambulance crew administered naloxone and raced her to hospital where her life was saved.

Polly became distraught when they threatened to keep her bairn in care. It jolted her into rehab. She started receiving a controlled dose of methadone, working less and eating more. John took note. Admired her for it. She deserved a break. Deserved something nice.

John retrieved a silver chain from his locker, one of many items found in Big Stu's boiler-suit pockets in the laundry and confiscated due to dubious provenance. It had been languishing unclaimed for one year, which meant it belonged to nobody now. At John's request, Jock dabbed a dod of solder on the bullet and fixed it to the chain. John gave Polly the necklace the next time a Senegalese boat came in.

Polly gave a tinkly chuckle of delight. John liked to see Polly happy again. She offered him a quickie for free, but he shook his head and told her she was like a daughter to him. Polly laughed at that, but not the good tinkly one, more of a hollow angry laugh. Then she looked sad again, so he fastened the chain round her slender neck with big awkward fingers, marvelling at the softness of her long hair as he pushed the rose-gold locks aside. She gave him a nice smile and kissed him on the cheek and said that John and Becksy were the only two men she knew to always turn down a freebie.

When the Jordanian phosphate rock ran out, the number

of false gas leaks reported to the gas board plummeted. Nobody believed John when he insisted that the gas smell came from the Jordanian phosphate rock. Factory chemists tested the materials and found no detectable difference in the level of impurities between the different sources, but they were looking for herds of sheep, not a tick on a single sheep, or fields of grass and not the lone seed on a single blade.

The problem never returned. Someone at head office drove a hard bargain with the Senegalese and supply returned exclusively to the cheerful, gentle and sweet-scented West Africans.

In the police interview room, John dangles the bullet on the end of the chain. It swings like a pendulum, the smooth silver petals glinting in the afternoon light shining through the barred window.

'1981,' he says. 'June or July, I can't be sure, but definitely 1981.'

The detective inspector scribbles something down and then pauses, pen mid-air. 'What's the story?' she asks.

'A bullet,' John hands the necklace back to the detective inspector and waits as she inspects it with new interest. 'From Jordan. It came to Leith hidden in seven thousand tonnes of phosphate rock. Exploded in the intake shaft. In the summer of 1981.'

'Anyone hurt?'

'No.'

'Summer of 1981?' She gets to her feet using the table for support. 'Stay here,' she instructs.

He lets out a long breath as she leaves. He didn't mention Polly. There is no need to mention Polly because the body in the phosphate cave is not hers.

There is nothing John is more certain of than that.

Third Clue

ABERDEEN KEYRING

POTASH

Eleven

Aberdeen Keyring

The day is not over, but the light in the police interview room dims by the second once the detective inspector leaves. The fierce, weak sun slides behind Corstorphine Hill – an angry bairn all tuckered out – and the room swims in soft, rosy light. A glint of red from the evidence tray catches John's eye.

He glances around the empty room, shrugs and picks up a key ring: the brass hoop connected by three chain-links to a metal plaque. It fills his palm, a pretty thing. Solid, a pleasing weight in the hand. Too big for a trouser pocket, too cumbersome for house or car keys. An anchor for the keys to something important.

The grease shed.

John strokes the plaque with his thumb. It glides over the smooth enamelled metal, traversing the ridges of the embossed design. Three silver towers stand proud against a red sky, flanked by yellow beasts, leopards rampant on muscular hind legs with paws outstretched.

Kelly's cats.

John glances at the clock. Three in the afternoon. February. Already dark in the Silver City.

He'd visited Aberdeen twice, once for work and once on holiday.

The guide on the *Taste of Scotland* coach tour told the group that Robert the Bruce laid siege to the castle and destroyed it along with English power. The city gate was removed to widen the roads, the church on St Katherine's Hill demolished. When Aberdeen was rebuilt in stone, it became the Silver City. The mica in the granite made the stone sparkle in the sunshine. Unfortunately, it was raining on the day the tour bus drove through Aberdeen city centre, so he never saw it for himself.

He stroked the raised surface of the medieval towers depicted on the key ring. Nothing is permanent. Nothing remains the same.

It was Corky, one of the potash drivers, who brought the news about Stinky Miller's. At first, John refused to believe him.

John peers at the city motto written in curly script at the bottom of the key ring.

'Bon Accord,' he reads out loud and then shakes his head. 'Bon Betrayal more like.'

Twelve

Potash

Potash is the name given to a range of natural salts of potassium[27]. It was Humphry Davy[(x)], a brilliant Cornish chemist and poet, who first isolated potassium metal. Davy is also remembered as the inventor of a safety lamp for miners and for naming laughing gas, although he quipped that his greatest ever discovery was Michael Faraday[(xiii)], the young man he hired to help after an accident in the lab damaged Davy's eyesight[28].

In 1807, Davy passed an electric current through a solution of potash and, after many false starts, punctuated by sparks, burns and explosions, finally isolated the element he was seeking.

Potassium is a silvery-white metal, soft enough to cut with a dinner knife. You may remember a school chemistry experiment demonstrating the increasing reactivity of Group 1 metals[29]. Your teacher donned a white coat, goggles and gloves and, with all the theatre a fine performer can muster, ordered the class to retreat to a safe distance. Unscrewing the lid from a little glass vial containing a silvery lump in a clear, protective oil, teasing out a little pearl with tweezers, dropping a nubbin of metal onto a dish of water. If the metal bead was lithium or sodium, it sizzled and raced across the surface in mad zigzags, a metal hovercraft on a raft of hydrogen. But if it spontaneously burst into flames, the hydrogen igniting and burning with tongues of lilac fire as it popped and jumped and danced across the water, then the metal was potassium.

Potassium is highly reactive, which is why you never find elemental potassium in nature. Humphry Davy had to use electrochemistry to coax it out of hiding when, all the time, it was right there in plain sight.

There are over five-hundred trillion[30] tonnes of potassium in the sea alone. Potassium reacts with oxygen to form flaky white potassium peroxide, and it reacts with water to form potassium hydroxide, a strong alkali which in turn will react with almost anything acidic to form stable potassium salts. Most potassium salts are soluble, so when it rains, the potassium compounds in the rocks and the soil are washed into the sea.

Life cannot thrive without potassium. Every single cell in your body contains potassium; the total weight in an average human body is about three hundred grams[1]. It's our enzyme activator and water controller. You need nitrogen for protein building and phosphorus for energy regulation, but potassium is key to communication inside the body. Signals from our senses are transferred across nerves via potassium ions. They control how we respond to stimuli and transmit impulses to and from the brain.

Potassium is even more concentrated in plants, especially in dried apricots, bananas, all nuts (especially almonds and pistachios), potatoes and avocados. It is essential for plant protein synthesis and regulates growth, determining the uptake of carbon dioxide through photosynthesis. Plants take potassium from the soil. In order to grow healthy plants, the potassium must be constantly replenished.

Natural forms of potassium include our old friend guano.

Organic farms can also use liquefied comfrey, seaweed meal, composted bracken, compost that is rich in decayed banana peels, and most importantly – wood ash.

Once upon a time it was ash burners who provided the potassium farmers needed. Gathering dead wood and the ashes from household fires, they carried it home in sacks and handcarts and tipped the ash into wicker baskets lined with linen which sat above the leaching vats. They poured water over the ash until all the salts were dissolved, then recovered them by evaporating the solution in large iron pots over a wood fire to obtain a valuable white residue: potassium carbonate.

Forests receded, households replaced wood with coal, but it was deep mine technology that finally put the ash burners out of a job.

Sylvite is an evaporite, a mineral formed by the evaporation of ancient oceans, potassium chloride being one of the last solids to crystallise out when seawater evaporates in the sun.

The Zechstein Sea once covered much of what is now Britain, The Netherlands, Denmark, Northern Germany, Poland and the waters in-between. Then, approximately 252 million years ago, came the Great Dying, the Permian–Triassic extinction. Whether the cause was meteor strikes or volcanic eruptions or a massive release of underground methane gas, the earth's climate changed, and up to 96 per cent of all marine species and 70 per cent of terrestrial vertebrate species became extinct. As the planet warmed, the Zechstein sea receded by evaporation, leaving behind thick a layer of salt. All the hard work of potassium concentration was done by the sun over millions of years. Over millennia, the evaporites were buried under layers of sand and mud which hardened into stone.

The discovery of potash underground put the ash burners out of a job, but it still takes extraordinary effort to bring it to the surface.

The village of Boulby lies about half-way down Great Britain's eastern shoreline, south of the river Tees and north of Whitby. The little seaside settlement on this beautiful sandy coast is dominated by the long white buildings, chimneys, gantries and winding gear of Cleveland Potash.

After sinking a shaft over one kilometre below the ground, extraction of sylvite began in 1969, and the mine now extends far into the salt layer, with thousands of kilometres of tunnels spreading out under the North Sea towards Denmark.

It's hot down there in the deep mine, and quiet under 1,100 metres of rock. A great place for a scientific laboratory.

Boulby Underground Laboratory is a multi-disciplinary deep underground science facility. Experiments can be carried out almost entirely free of interference from background radiation, in particular from natural 'cosmic rays' which perpetually bombard the Earth's surface. Studies into geology and geophysics, climate, the environment, life in extreme environments and the search for the missing sub-atomic particles that make up 85 per cent of the universe are all conducted down there.

Over a thousand metres under the North Sea, scientists are searching for Dark Matter in a potash mine.

Thirteen

Stinky Miller's

Potash came to the Leith fertiliser factory from far underground, from a place that John called the North Yorkshire Sea. The mineshafts plunged down deeper than Scotland's highest mountains would go if inverted and pushed, peak first, into the earth.

Every day, a convoy of lorries arrived at the Leith Fertiliser Works from the North Yorkshire mine. The potash drivers were a valuable source of information on the inner workings of the Agricultural Division of Imperial Chemical Industries. News was relayed from the mouth of one working man to the ear of another. The carrier pigeons of intelligence, the same men who supplied the main Billingham site in Teesside also delivered a rich guano of gossip to the satellite factories of Aberdeen and Leith, along with lorry-loads of granular pink potash.

The powder was transported in open wagons, driven by red-faced men with paunches and piles. Fine particles of potash blew into the broken windows of the cabs and the drivers arrived tired and filthy. Most lorries offloaded into the whalebone sheds at Leith, but a few were sent on to the smaller factory, Sandilands, in Aberdeen.

Stinky Miller's, as Sandilands was known locally, was much older than the Leith plant. It had opened in 1848 when the raw materials for fertiliser were blood and bone from the abattoir, spoiled fish from the trawlers, bones and guts from the fish-processing factory, and barrels of condemned offal. Life recycled. The stench from the chemical works came from the natural ingredients: the artificial fertiliser produced later was odourless.

Except when someone in head office bought Jordanian instead of Senegalese phosphate rock.

At Stinky Miller's (the name stuck) the reactors were built of wood. A giant wooden barrel shovelled full of phosphate rock was sealed before adding sulphuric acid through lead pipes. Wooden paddles mixed the solid and liquid as they reacted to form superphosphate.

As the old carpenters retired, it became harder to find young men both skilled enough to maintain the wooden vats and mixers and hardy enough to work in the oldest factory in Aberdeen. The boom of North Sea Oil, new and shiny and much better paid, created a vacuum into which the skilled and the strong disappeared.

Over time, the potash transfers to Aberdeen became few and far between.

John was on his way to breakfast when Corky hailed him from the cab of a potash lorry. John ignored him. A man of inflexible routine, when on day shift John was always the first person to step through the door of the canteen at one minute past eight o'clock in the morning. The canteen staff started opening the four sliding bolts on the double doors at eight o'clock and each one took a few seconds. It took him six minutes to walk from the shift supervisor's office to the canteen and he always left at five minutes to eight. Sharp. On the dot. If anyone tried to detain him on the way he simply walked through them. Not past them, with a dismissive wave to indicate that they should come back later. Not pausing to wish a cheery good morning and an invitation to join him. He didn't alter a step, neither pace nor direction, seeing nothing except his target, the opening canteen door.

His breakfast, on day shift, was always a fried egg on a slice of square, pink, Lorne sausage placed in a floury white bap.

In one of many rounds of cutbacks, the managers' dining room was merged with the workers' canteen. John did not approve: it stifled the banter and prevented his men from enjoying the break they deserved. He grudgingly acknowledged an improvement in the standards of hygiene and the range and quality of the food. It didn't affect him at breakfast, but it often spoiled the main meal of his day.

John's seating position at lunchtime was a useful barometer of industrial relations. The managers always sat beside the window. Usually John sat at the next table in, close enough to exchange pleasantries but far enough away to maintain proper respect for rank. However, if there had been a major injustice – a night shift unfairly blamed for some interruption to production or a lily-livered proposal to soften up on some ancient rule – he would sit as far away as possible.

He always took the soup, coming back for more as a compliment to the cook, and then a main course hidden under a mound of potatoes and gravy. He never ate pudding.

The canteen hours made no sense to John. They mirrored the office hours: closing at night, weekends and public holidays. The factory was manned twenty-four hours a day, seven days a week, fifty-two and a quarter weeks per year. The people who most needed a hot meal were the shift workers who started earlies at 6am, back shift at 2pm or nights at 10pm. Few of the workers had cars, so they cycled in or took a public bus and then walked through the docks. Edinburgh buses were rare before 6am or after 10pm, so it was a long trudge, especially if one of the swing bridges was open to let a ship through and the men had to take the detour round Victoria dock. Despite automation, a lot of the factory work was still manual: digging, shovelling, packing, tightening, hammering. The office staff, on the other hand, drove to work and then barely moved.

The problem, they told him, was that the canteen was manned by women, and women didn't work shifts. Tell that to the nurses and office cleaners, John muttered.

Contractors, such as lorry drivers, were banned from all factory amenities, including the canteen: the subsidised meals were for employees only. Having failed to get John's attention earlier, Corky, one of the regular potash lorry drivers, was waiting for John at the gatehouse when he finished breakfast. On this particular morning, Corky looked and smelt terrible. John wrinkled his nose and listened.

Corky had taken a load of potash from Boulby to Aberdeen only to find the factory gates chained and to be told that they were accepting no more deliveries. His instructions were to take his load back to Leith. He had been twelve hours on the road and asked John for permission to take a shower before the long drive back. It was a reasonable request but even so, John had to think about it. Harry, the amenities cleaner who only worked days, was on duty, and the first shift changeover was several hours away. John agreed on the basis that he would personally inspect the shower after the driver had finished.

The next week John was on his days off. Word had got around among the contract drivers. One was seen leaving the amenities block and challenged. He assured the duty shift manager that drivers were now allowed to use the showers.

The duty shift manager was uncomfortable, but on learning that it had been agreed with John, decided not to intervene. He knew that it was a recipe for trouble but didn't bother to avert disaster by restricting times of use to avoid shift changeovers or match the cleaners' hours.

It came to a head one Sunday. At shift changeover one of the operators found a trail of gritty brown potash over the wooden benches, leading across the tiled floor and ending in a nest of ginger hair floating above the blocked shower drain.

The union officials threatened industrial action. The factory management called a meeting.

After heated representations from the workforce, management agreed with the union to reinforce the existing rule: access to the amenity block was denied to anyone who was not a full-time employee – no exceptions permitted. John was publicly censured.

The union officials were so puffed up with their victory over John that they barely registered the next item on the agenda, the management decision to close the Aberdeen factory with the loss of eighty jobs.

John never forgave the Edinburgh shop stewards. The Aberdonians might have been members of a different union, but what was the point of the trade union movement if not solidarity? Exclusive use of the showers for employees meant the denial of a basic amenity to other working men. Drivers and contractors had no place to wash after work. More interested in protecting their own privileges at Leith, the Edinburgh unions had sold their Aberdeen colleagues out.

A rush of cold air rouses John from his reverie. The detective inspector glides into the interview room, letting the overenthusiastic spring slam the door shut behind her. At the crunch of the latch, metal on metal, the key ring jumps from John's hands, flipping over as it clatters onto the table. The initials WHAM are stamped on the back.

'After 1985,' John says as she eases herself into her seat.

'Getting closer.' She nods approvingly. 'What is it, a key ring?'

He nods. 'For the grease shed,' he says. 'First at Stinky Miller's, the Aberdeen Branch of the ess-ey-aye. Then at Leith.'

The detective inspector scribbles it down.

She pulls the key ring towards her, humming a snatch of music.

John stares at her, perplexed. She stops and blushes. 'The initials,' she explains and points to them: WHAM. '"Careless Whisper", "Soul on the Dole". Hits of the eighties.'

He looks at her, blankly.

'So, who did this belong to?'

'Tall Willy,' John says. 'William Hamish Angus MacDonald. The chief engineer moved to Leith when the Aberdeen site closed in 1985. He reused the key ring for a brand-new grease shed.'

'What's a grease shed?' she asks.

'Lube-re-cay-shun.' John says it slowly, emphasising each syllable as if it were a foreign word. 'Oil drums, grease pots.'

She looks bored.

'It's not the only thing here that belonged to Tall Willy,' John says, nodding at the tray of objects.

She looks interested.

'Tell me more,' she says.

Fourth Clue

AIR HORN

AMMONIA

Fourteen

Air Horn

Inside the police interview room, John picks up an air horn from the tray of evidence, one of ten objects found beside a dead body, identity unknown.

A canister of compressed air, the size of a beer can, with a red funnel. Designed for use at sea, the tin is decorated with simple coloured blocks representing a ferry, a yacht, and an inflatable life-raft.

'Don't...' The detective inspector begins, but it is too late.

She clasps her hands over her ears as a blast of sound pierces the air and echoes from the walls.

'Sorry,' John says, but he is not sorry. It is a good sound, the sound of safety, the sound of disaster averted. A sound that once resonated from the eastern corner of the fertiliser factory. Of course, it sounds quite different in the police interview room, harsh and strident without a huge metal bell to soften and temper it. But it is a sound that brings back good memories.

In 1985, the chief engineer of Stinky Miller's removed the factory keys from their enamelled key ring and handed them over to the demolition contractor. Wiping away a mote of dust from his eye, he drove to Leith. The only good outcome from the Aberdeen plant closure was the arrival in Leith of a gifted engineer, William Hamish Angus MacDonald, known in both factories as Tall Willy.

Whenever John thought about Tall Willy, he could almost smell the ammonia.

Fifteen

Ammonia

As any attentive school pupil could tell you, the Haber process wrenches super-stable nitrogen from the air and bludgeons it into a form more useful to humanity.

Fritz Haber[xxi], a German chemist, was awarded the Nobel Prize for chemistry in 1918 for his ammonia process. A little local difficulty prevented him from receiving his prize until 1919.

Ammonia-based fertilisers improved crop yields and prevented billions of people from starving to death. Ironic that ammonia's first use was to make war munitions and that Mr Haber is also the father of chemical weapons, leader of a team who successfully weaponised chlorine during the First World War.

In fact, ammonia synthesis should be known as the Haber-Bosch[D] process, but we often forget Carl Bosch[xxiii], who led the team to scale up the Haber process. Carl Bosch also received a Nobel Prize for chemistry, although later, in 1931.

In the Haber-Bosch process, nitrogen and hydrogen react over a catalyst to make ammonia. Scaling up a novel laboratory process to industrial scale is never simple, especially when high temperatures and pressures are involved.

Carl Bosch faced three challenges.

The first was to find an economic source of the raw materials.

Nitrogen makes up 78 per cent of the air we breathe. You can separate it from oxygen and argon and the other gases in air by cooling until it becomes liquid[D1]. How you cool to minus two hundred degrees centigrade – using Joule-Thomson throttling – is REALLY interesting (trust me), but we're coming to that later.

The simplest method for producing hydrogen might be splitting water with electricity (as proposed by Haber), but this relies on cheap, continuous energy supplies.

Most of the hydrogen for ammonia production comes from natural gas. The overall reaction is methane plus water to give hydrogen plus carbon dioxide[D2]. Of course, it's a bit more complicated than that. If you've been paying attention, you'll remember that natural hydrocarbons came from living creatures so life (and death) contains sulphur. These organic sulphur compounds must be removed to avoid bad smells, corrosion and catalyst poisoning[D2.1]. The sulphur-free methane is mixed with high pressure steam[D2.2, D2.3]. For every tonne of hydrogen produced you also get nine tonnes of carbon dioxide[D2.4]. A little is collected, purified and sold (to put the fizz in carbonated drinks like Coca-Cola and fill fire extinguishers) but most goes straight out into the atmosphere. A little of the product hydrogen is sacrificed[D2.5] to remove any left-over traces of carbon monoxide or carbon dioxide (turning them back to methane) and a little more hydrogen goes back to the start of the process to remove the sulphur[D2.1].

So now you have your raw materials. What next?

The second challenge faced by Bosch was to replace the uranium-osmium catalyst. Osmium is extremely rare. Uranium is also expensive, radioactive and a tad unstable. After twenty thousand attempts, the team came up with a cheap and efficient magnetite[D4] catalyst that worked every bit as well.

So now you have your catalyst, what next?

Bosch's third challenge was the extreme reaction conditions. The forward reaction in the Haber process[D3] is favoured by high pressure, so the feed mixture is compressed to about two hundred atmospheres. The process is exothermic – heat is given out – so the backward reaction is favoured by high temperature. Which means that for complete conversion to ammonia, you should remove the heat and keep the temperature as low as possible. But if the temperature is too low, the reaction is very slow. A compromise must be found between speed of reaction (favoured by high temperatures) and conversion to ammonia (favoured by low temperatures). The compromise temperature chosen by Fritz Haber was 550 degrees centigrade.

Massive, thick-walled steel vessels would be required to contain any gas at such high temperatures and pressures, but these are not just any gases.

Hydrogen is a tricky little blighter, the smallest molecule in the periodic table of 118 elements with an uncanny ability to sneak into the tiniest gaps. When it escapes, it has a nasty habit of exploding. On its way, it reacts with everything in its path, even the tiny amounts of carbon used to temper steel, causing the metal to lose its strength.

The first reactor exploded after only eighty hours in operation. Bosch solved the problem by corralling the reacting gases into tubes. The tubes were lined with soft iron, free of carbon, but the tube strength came from the carbon-steel which encased it. He left spaces for any escaping hydrogen to be funnelled to safety.

It worked. The first industrial plant started producing

ammonia in Oppau, Germany in 1913 and by the following year was producing twenty tonnes per day[31].

Modern production of ammonia, in plants that can produce up to three thousand tonnes per day[32], takes place in multi-storey reactors where nitrogen and hydrogen flow through multiple beds of catalyst with cooling in-between. At the optimum temperature, the conversion rate to ammonia is about 20 per cent and the unreacted gases are recycled back to the start.

During the First World War, the Haber process provided Germany with a source of ammonia for the production of explosives, compensating for the Allied Powers' trade blockade on other sources.

Carl Bosch did receive a Nobel Prize, but his violent disagreements with the Nazi regime precipitated his dismissal from the company he helped found: IG Farben. While his former colleagues produced Zyklon B to murder millions in concentration camps, he turned to amateur astronomy, meteorite collecting and drink.

A British chemist and engineer was named on the Haber patent, and shared 40 per cent of the royalties. Robert Le Rossignol[(xxiv)] worked with Fritz Haber from 1906–1909, developing the tabletop apparatus that allowed Haber to demonstrate the high-pressure ammonia process, a way to 'make bread from the air'.

At the start of the First World War in 1914, while Fritz went off to supervise the murder of other Brits with chlorine gas, his friend and colleague Robert was interned in Germany, returning to the UK with his German wife and German-born sons after the end of the war. Sadly, his two sons were dead by the end of the Second World War, one taking his own life at Cambridge University after thinking he had failed his chemistry exams, the other, an RAF pilot, dying during the Italian campaign in 1943. Robert became a philanthropist, using the royalty income from the Haber patent to support charity.

One person rarely mentioned is Dr Clara Immerwahr[(xxii)], herself a brilliant chemist. The first woman to be awarded a doctorate in chemistry at a German university, she was unable to continue her own research after marriage to Fritz Haber, becoming his assistant instead. She violently opposed her husband's work on chemical weapons, declaring it a 'perversion of the ideals of science' and 'a sign of barbarity, corrupting the very discipline which ought to bring new insights into life.'[33] In 1915 Clara and Fritz quarrelled as he prepared to travel to the Eastern front to supervise a chlorine gas attack. She took his pistol and shot herself. He left anyway; it took her several days to die.

Whatever you think of his personal qualities, the process that Fritz Haber invented underpinned the 'Green Revolution' in agriculture. At the end of the nineteenth century, scientists were predicting world famine due to a shortage of fixed nitrogen. With rising populations, agriculture had become more intensive and natural sources of nitrogen were running out.

Manure from animals spread on fields recycles only part of the nitrogen they extracted from the soil in the first place. Most excreted nitrogen ends up in sewage works and much of the nitrogen accumulated in animal bodies is lost to the air during cremation.

One source of new nitrogen in the soil comes from lightning strikes. The high energy from the electrical discharge breaks the strong bond between atoms in a molecule of nitrogen and allows it to react with oxygen to form rain-soluble nitrates.

A small number of plants can fix nitrogen from the air. Clover, alfalfa and lupin have symbiotic bacteria in nodules on their roots that convert nitrogen in the air into ammonia that can be used by the plant. The nitrate compounds produced remain available to other plants after the nitrogen-fixing plant dies. Crop rotation with such plants, a green manure, has many advantages for the long-term health of the soil, but it puts productive land out of use and reduces the short-term food supply.

Fixed nitrogen, the nitrogen available to our bodies in solid or liquid form, is constantly disappearing into the air. Lightning strikes, soil bacteria and plants with nitrogen-fixing nodules in their root systems fix some of the nitrogen from the air back into the soil, but without the process for making ammonia from air, there would be fewer of us alive today. And if we stopped using artificial fertiliser tomorrow, many of us would starve.

Sixteen

Rail Tanker Derailment

The Leith factory was too small to have its own ammonia synthesis plant, so every day six pressurised rail tankers containing anhydrous ammonia travelled 150 miles from ICI Billingham on the busy east coast railway linking London with Inverness. On arrival the pressurised liquid was transferred into one of three huge spherical storage tanks, kept refrigerated and under pressure, with enough storage capacity for a few days' production.

Before offloading the rail tankers into the spheres, John would always check there was enough room. He didn't trust the instruments: he preferred to lower the temperature so he could see for himself. If the liquid inside the sphere was below zero degrees centigrade, a thin layer of ice formed on the outside. The visible level of ice mirrored the invisible level of liquid ammonia inside.

The rail tankers were not refrigerated, so they had to be built to withstand a much higher pressure than the storage tanks. In strong sunshine, even in Scotland, the temperature on the metal surface of the rail tankers could reach thirty degrees centigrade, so the pressure could rise to twelve times atmospheric pressure.

John was on shift when the call came from British Rail. One of the ammonia rail tankers had derailed. They needed the company's permission to lift it back onto the tracks.

No.

John told them firmly and clearly not to touch the tanker. Someone from the company would supervise. He took full details and promised to dispatch a team immediately.

In the gatehouse Blind Willy was ready with his sheet of Braille. The emergency protocol initiated, within a few minutes police, fire, chemical emergency specialists and a head office engineer were on their way to the scene. The operators took note of stocks and started to turn down the production rates. A derailed tanker meant a prolonged slow-down. No further shipments of ammonia would be made until the root cause was established and fixed.

When John arrived at the scene of the accident the rail tanker was still intact, but four wheels of the bogie had jumped the rail, causing the tanker barrel to tilt at an alarming angle. John wasn't taking any chances. By the time the rest of the team arrived, all trains had been diverted, the access road sealed off, and the occupants of two houses nearby temporarily evacuated. A road tanker was brought up and close-coupled, a water curtain set up. The ammonia was transferred from the rail to the road tanker. Huge slings were wrapped round the belly of the stricken container. Once it was empty and secure, it was decoupled and lifted with a crane onto a flatbed lorry.

Meanwhile the wheel tapper inspected the other bogies. With a large iron hammer, he struck each of the wheels in turn and listened to the ring. The slightest imperfection, a hairline crack would be enough to dull the sound. They all rang true. The head office engineer carried out a final inspection of each wagon in minute detail and finally gave the go-ahead to close the incident and move the convoy to the factory.

The press arrived looking for a story just as the train was moving out. A reporter from the *Evening Times* spotted the high hazard labels on the rail cars. In the days before the internet, he had to call the company emergency number for information. A highly trained communications professional reassured him that there was absolutely no danger to the public.

The intrepid reporter waited until after normal office hours before phoning the factory pretending to be from the rail safety team. A young engineer, not long out of university, was the last to leave the office block that day. She was preparing to turn off the lights and lock up when the phone rang. The gravelly voice of Alec, the gateman, informed her that British Rail wanted to speak to someone who knew about chemistry. Was there anyone still there? She informed him that she was perfectly capable of handling technical queries. He snorted and put the call through. If there had been a phone transcript, it would have looked something like this.

Can you confirm what was in the rail tanker that jumped the rails?
Ammonia.
Is it dangerous?
It might be better if you talked to…
This is very urgent.
You're from British Rail Safety, right?
Mmmhmmm.
So, you have the material safety data sheet.
Yes, of course…(rustling)…but can you talk me through it?
Look, I should get someone else to call you back…
No, please. Sorry if my questions sound daft, but I'm new here.
Me too (laughs).
I'd be really grateful.

OK, fire away. I'll answer what I can.

Is it dangerous?

Well...(pause)...yes and no.

Tell me more.

Ammonia is one of the good gases. You can smell it long before it does you any harm. Your eyes start to water. It makes you cough. If you smell it, the advice is to move away, upwind if you can.

What if you can't?

It's soluble in water. A wet cloth over nose and mouth if you can.

And if you can't?

Then it can damage your lungs.

Would that kill you?

If you breathe it in at too high a concentration for too long, then yes. Even few grams can harm you.

A few grams?

If you're in direct contact, in a confined space.

How much ammonia was in the rail tanker?

Twenty-five tonnes.

And there were six of them in the convoy, right?

Yes.

And you store more ammonia on site?

Yes.

So how much in total?

The maximum? Let's see... (scratch of pen on paper)...about four hundred tonnes.

How many people could that kill?

If it was all released at once?

Yes.

That's hardly a credible scenario.

But you've planned for every contingency, right? So, what's the worst-case scenario?

I'm really not the right person...

Humour me.

Well, theoretically, if you released everything at once it could wipe out most of Edinburgh. But look, this isn't like Bhopal.

Bhopal, what's that?

You haven't heard of the Bhopal accident? In India?

India, right. Rings a bell.

December 1984. Thousands of people killed by the release of a toxic gas. Hundreds of thousands injured.

How much released?

Forty tonnes.

And you have four hundred, right?

But you can't compare. Look, I didn't get your name...

(Click)... (Brrrrrrrrr)...

The phone went dead.

The young engineer scratched her head. What a peculiar conversation. She hadn't said anything that the rail safety team didn't already know, so why did she have the disquieting feeling that she'd messed up?

It was perfectly true that if the complete contents of the three spheres and all the rail wagons were to simultaneously split open and release their contents into a light onshore wind, with a temperature inversion preventing it from dispersing into the stratosphere, then most of North Edinburgh lay in the path of the resulting cloud.

It was also correct that the number of people who lived in the affected area would number hundreds of thousands.

Furthermore, it was accurate to say that if you breathed steadily in a cloud of ammonia at a concentration of a few per cent then you would probably die of lung damage.

But you can smell ammonia long before it does you any harm. At five parts per million, in fact. That's a bucket in an Olympic-sized swimming pool, a clod of turf kicked out of a football pitch, a small flock of sheep in the whole of Wales. Go inside, close all the doors and windows, cover your nose and mouth with a damp cloth.

Risk equals hazard multiplied by probability.

Factories that store ammonia are required to have multiple safeguards – layers of protection starting with a tried and trusted design, regular inspections, trained operators, a refrigeration system with backup, safety relief valves venting at high level into a prevailing offshore wind, alarms and shut-down systems, and if all else fails, an emergency response with water curtains and foam blankets.

With all the safeguards in place, the probability of mass fatalities from an ammonia release was about the same as the likelihood of Arthur's seat turning into an active volcano and dousing the unsuspecting population in pyrophoric ash. Or an earthquake in the North Sea sending a tidal wave roaring up the Firth of Forth and three-hundred-metre-high waves engulfing the population.

But the damage was done. 'Toxic time bomb – A Scottish Bhopal but TEN TIMES WORSE', read the headline the next day.

Even before the *Evening Times* headline, no one in the company was complacent. The safeguards involved in keeping the population of North Edinburgh safe from harm were extensive.

One of those safeguards was refrigeration.

Seventeen

Thermodynamics

When the sun shone on the ammonia storage spheres, the contents began to warm, despite a thick layer of insulation. The energy from the sun caused the cold liquid to evaporate and the temperature and pressure in the spheres began to rise. The pressure could be lowered by sucking away the ammonia gas to feed production.

If you remove the gas above a liquid, some liquid evaporates, vaporising or 'flashing off' to replace the lost gas, and this causes cooling, just like when you sweat. So sending the ammonia as flash gas to the production plants reduced both the pressure and temperature in the storage spheres.

It had other benefits as well, although these weren't fully appreciated until later.

But if the Granny or Nitram plants weren't running, the pressure in the ammonia spheres had to be lowered in another way.

Using the Joule-Thomson effect[34].

James Prescott Joule[xv] was born in 1818. Fascinated by electricity as a child, he experimented by giving shocks to family members and servants. To keep him out of trouble, he was given the family brewery to run. Good call. The practical and economic challenges proved inspirational to the amateur scientist. He was the first to experimentally prove a connection between heat and work.

So dedicated was Joule to his science, he invited a friend along on his honeymoon to measure the temperature differences between the top and bottom of waterfalls in Chamonix.

His waterfall honeymoon friend was William Thomson[xvi] who later became the famous Lord Kelvin. In 1852 the two men showed how gases and liquids drop in temperature as they expand.

How did his new wife, Amelia Joule, née Grimes[xiv], feel about thermodynamics on her honeymoon? Did her feelings toward her husband cool? Was she tempted to throttle him?

Cooling with throttling is called the Joule-Thomson effect.

It's hard to find a cooling medium for something that's already cold. For ammonia in the spheres at zero degrees centigrade, you'd need something significantly colder to remove the heat. Dry ice or liquid nitrogen might work but those options are impractical and expensive.

However, if you pressurise the gas, you don't need dry ice or liquid nitrogen to cool it down, you can condense it into a liquid just using the Scottish weather.

When you do work on something, like squeezing a gas to increase its pressure, the temperature rises. What's the point of that, you ask, I thought we were trying to cool things down? We are, but sometimes you must take one step back to go two steps forward, climb a hill before descending into a valley deeper than the plain you started from. Compressing a gas makes it easier to condense it into a liquid. And when you drop the pressure of that liquid, it cools right back down.

That's how your fridge works. And, in reverse, that's how heat pumps work.

You need energy to turn a liquid into a gas, for example when you boil a kettle. Energy has to be removed from a gas to turn it back into a liquid, roughly the same amount whether it is at low temperature and pressure or at a higher temperature and pressure.

With ammonia pressurised to fifteen atmospheres, you only need to cool the gas to below forty degrees centigrade to persuade it to condense. With an average air temperature in Leith of ten degrees centigrade (plus or minus ten), the same as the average seawater temperature, plus or minus five, the hot pressurised gas can be easily cooled.

The ammonia gas at Leith was squeezed between the spinning blades of a high-speed compressor. The heated gas raced through a coiled pipe which snaked first through air and then cascading seawater. The hot, pressurised gas inside the coil condensed to form a liquid.

The pressurised liquid was still hot, before it passed through a throttling valve. The drop in pressure caused some of the liquid to flash off as a gas, just as it does when you open a pressure cooker. The cool ammonia liquid returned to the spheres and the ammonia gas went around the refrigeration circuit again.

Like your fridge, an industrial refrigeration plant is powered by electricity. On normal days this came from the grid. The Scottish Central Electricity Generating Board harnessed the power of highland waterfalls. Hydroelectric turbines, driven by falling water, spun magnets in copper coils to produce electricity for the ammonia refrigeration plant compressors.

In the case of a power cut, diesel-powered generators would start up automatically to keep the refrigeration plant running. The backup generators were too small to run the whole factory, designed to be just sufficient for the safety-critical operations: keeping the lights on, the fire pumps primed, the compressed air to the safety valves, and ensuring the hazardous ammonia remained cool and contained in the spheres rather than boiling and escaping as a toxic cloud creeping over the city of Edinburgh.

Refrigeration is energy-intensive and inefficient. More heat is generated at the back of your fridge than is removed inside it. Opening the fridge door to cool your kitchen will have the opposite effect.

Energy can be transformed from one form to another, but it can't be created or destroyed. The work done by Scottish waterfalls was mainly dissipated as heat (just as James Prescott Joule and his honeymoon companion always suspected).

The heat removed from the ammonia spheres had to go somewhere; it warmed the air around Leith and the seawater in the Firth of Forth, leading to an infinitesimally tiny increase in temperature.

Thanks to the Joule-Thomson effect, the ammonia in the storage spheres was kept cold at a pressure that could be contained, but refrigeration was only part of the story. The safety of the residents of North Edinburgh depended on more than just refrigeration, it depended on the mechanical integrity of the spheres.

Eighteen

Inflatable Boat

The ammonia storage spheres were made of metal, multiple plates of special steel welded together. Keeping the ammonia inside its metal shell required constant vigilance. And maintenance.

Tall Willy, the engineer who moved to Leith from Aberdeen, was more used to wood than steel. So ICI sent him on courses, and he did his own reading. His chief concern became stress corrosion cracking. A combination of chlorides from the sea and the ever-cycling internal pressure, rising during the day and falling at night, made the steel of the spheres the perfect target for this slow and insidious form of rot. Unlike rust, another form of corrosion, it was impossible to detect without close inspection of the inside surface.

It's easy to test for stress corrosion cracking in a laboratory. You take a sample, slice though the metal and look for cracks under the microscope. That is called destructive testing. Non-destructive testing (where you leave the structure intact) is harder. Tall Willy had settled on dye penetration testing, starting with the places where the residual fabrication stress was highest: on welds, around manholes and nozzles – the points where pipes enter and leave.

First you paint the surface with a pink dye. Bright girly pink. Then you spray a white powder over it. If the metal below is smooth, it looks like fresh snow. Where there are cracks or imperfections, the pink dye bleeds through.

The problem was the access. Or rather the cost of access. Or more accurately, the lack of provision in the maintenance budget by Willy's predecessor for the cost of access. Tall Willy had to find savings every year even as the demands of the ageing plant increased. The cost of scaffolding inside one of the spheres to allow him to reach every square centimetre of the interior was tens of thousands of pounds. The recommended regime for internal inspection every three years meant budgeting to inspect one of the three spheres every year.

Tall Willy knew that if he went to the company technical safety committee, they would support him. The problem was that Billingham had excess capacity and this would be the perfect excuse to shut down the ammonia storage at Leith. And everything it fed. Nitric acid. Ammonium nitrate. Granulation. Jobs. The second of a thousand cuts.

Tall Willy was out fishing when the idea came to him. It was a perfect day. Cold and wet meant quiet. Only the gentle wind in the trees and the soft rain falling into the tumbling river disturbed the silence. He was casting from the riverbank, idly watching a tangle of red-gold leaves and twigs caught up in a fallen tree. It was raining on the hills and the river was in spate. As he watched the level of the water rise, the branch wedged between the riverbed and the bank barely moved, but the floating autumn raft of debris rose higher and higher until it cleared the obstruction and sailed off down the river.

Willy bought an inflatable boat for £20. He filled the empty, clean sphere with water. An Olympic swimming pool-worth of water. He threw the boat in and inflated it through the manhole. Then he climbed down a rope ladder and paddled round the inside of the sphere. When he was ready to descend, he sounded a foghorn and his assistant opened the drain valve to let some water out: fifty bathtubs-worth for every metre of descent by the time he was halfway down.

Whenever he found a pink imperfection, he sounded the foghorn twice and marked it with a permanent, waterproof marker. By the time he was at the bottom, he had marked out seven repairs and his assistant outside had noted the exact height of each one, based on the volume of water discharged from the sphere through a totalising flowmeter. Willy didn't attempt any hot work from his boat. Simple platforms were erected to reach the seven repairs, the defects were ground out, welded, stress-relieved and tested again.

Water played an important part in other ways. Willy was able to confirm the theory that adding a tiny amount of water to the ammonia significantly reduced the appearance of stress corrosion cracking. Inspections were gradually extended to every six years, and Willy's boat was not required as often.

His initiative was copied throughout the company, saving millions, and Tall Willy was promoted to chief engineer. He saved enough on his maintenance budget to buy a proper, clean lockable shed for lubricants, just like the one he had insisted on at Stinky Miller's, and attached the new keys to the old Aberdeen key fob. The number of breakdowns on the site fell dramatically.

As John sings the praises of the chief engineer to Detective Inspector Rose Irvine, she begins to fidget. Twirling a strand of strawberry blonde hair round a finger, she leans forward and looks John in the eye.

'If the keyring and air horn were his, could the body be that of...' she pauses to check the initials on the keyring. 'William Hamish Angus MacDonald?'

John looks at the photos on the desk.

'How tall was the victim?' he asks.

Rose picks up the phone. 'Anything back from forensics?'

A knock at the door and a uniformed officer hands her a typed note. She reads it and frowns.

'Still no useful results.' She crumples the note into a little ball and mutters. 'Just a list of excuses. What's keeping them?'

'Tall Willy is six-foot-four.' John says. 'And last I heard he was driving steam engines on the West Highland line.'

The detective inspector sighs. 'Let's wrap it up for today.'

'Aye.'

'There's a few things I need to do.'

A few backsides that need kicking, thinks John, looking at the ball of paper.

'You've been most helpful.' When Rose smiles, it lights up the room. 'At least we've established that the victim probably perished between...' she checks her notes, '1985 and 1997. I'll check out missing persons in that timeframe.'

Detective Inspector Rose Irvine stands and opens the door.

'If you think of anything else,' she says, 'You know where to find me.'

John glances at the other objects on the tray.

'Aye.'

Although it is cold outside and his hip aches, he decides to walk a little. To clear his mind. To stop off in a crowded pub. To use the warm fug of strangers to muffle his growing doubts, to relive the days of simple, uncomplicated companionship.

He doubles back to Athol Place, walks round the north side of the crescent and finds a pub on William Street. It's not his sort of place. Lawyers, accountants and embassy folk drinking cocktails. Buckets of ice and glass decanters. Music that is more mood than melody.

If you think of anything else...

How can John think of anything else? His brain is so full of the people and stories from the factory that there is no room left. Worse than that, there are noises in his head: a ringing of bogie wheels, a muffled horn, a clatter of scaffold poles, the crash of waves against the dock. A fledgling thought stretches the corners of his mind, cracking the carapace of control, shapeless, dark and ill-defined.

He strikes up conversation with a group of lassies, but it only chases them away. He orders a second pint and resolves to get a bus home.

Whatever is trying to emerge from his memories, it is something bad.

Something very bad.

Nineteen

Tiramisu

John is not easy to find.

His address turns out to be the top floor flat of a granite-grey block of flats overlooking the slate-grey Water of Leith. With a bell that doesn't work.

The detective inspector stands at the main door of the tenement, gazes up at the high windows and sighs, wishing she had sent a constable instead. She pumps the brass bell pull for flat 3/5 until the pads of her fingers stick to the icy metal. No answer. She inserts her left pinkie in the T-shaped keyhole of the main door to spring the latch. Ouch! As the door clicks open, a sharp burr catches her finger. She wipes away a tiny bead of blood and pops the finger into her mouth, tasting metal and salt as she pushes the heavy door open. The stone stairs are lit by a skylight high above. Each step has a dip in the middle, worn by years of footfall.

Rose grasps the wooden bannister and climbs slowly, pausing after each flight of stairs until she reaches the fifth floor where John's name is engraved on a steel plaque next to a modern buzzer. She presses the button. Hears it ring. No answer. She balls her hand into a fist and raps on the door.

From the floor below, a chain rattles and a door creaks open. A wavering voice calls up.

'Youse looking for big Jonno?'

'Aye.'

'No in trouble again, is he?'

A white-haired old biddy, food stains splattering the front of her coat, peers through the chain-width gap between door and frame. The stench of mould grows more intense as the policewoman descends the stairs.

'Now, why would John be in trouble?' Rose asks, always alert, always suspicious. This is a potential murder inquiry after all.

The old wifey sniffs. 'A good lad, is Jonno.'

'Then he won't mind talking to us.'

The old woman shivers and pulls her outer coat closer. It is one of many, she is layered against the cold. 'Whit fer?'

'Canna say.' The policewoman shakes her head and squares her shoulders. 'Where is John?'

'Canna say.' The old woman closes the door.

John is not difficult to find. The checkout girl at the closest Tesco Express, where Rose stops to buy a bottle of Irn-Bru, a packet of crisps and a Twix, tells her exactly where he has lunch every day.

'What's he done this time?'

'This time?'

But the girl is interrupted by an impatient customer and a queue is forming. Best to return when it is quieter. Rose leaves her car parked outside the shop and crosses the road. She is still pondering as she walks down the steep hill to Canonmills.

The Italian café rises from the bridge and juts out over the Water of Leith. The small windows are fogged, but Rose can see tea-lights in frosted glass holders on red-checked table-cloths. A bell clangs as she enters, and a young woman in an apron bustles forward, her cascade of auburn curls almost as wide as she is tall.

'Table for one?'

For a moment, Rose is lost for words. Warm scents of Mediterranean cooking – oregano, thyme, garlic – are doing something to her salivary glands; her ears ring with the clatter of cutlery on colourful earthenware, the hum of easy conversation, the hubbub of a busy eatery; her fingers itch to reach out and brush the silky curls that frame the young woman's welcoming smile. In another life, could this have been her regular too? Instead of a bottle of skooshy in the car accompanied by processed fat, salt and more sugar? All the food groups. All the things the doctor told her to cut out.

She pulls herself together. 'I'm looking for John Gibson.'

The waitress nods. 'John,' she shouts over her shoulder. 'Youse two-timing me again?'

Rose frowns at the waitress and flashes the police ID in her wallet.

The waitress remains unfazed. 'She says she's buying.'

John is seated at the back, next to the kitchen, deep in conversation with a man in chef's whites. When John sees Rose, he gets to his feet, a hand flying to his mouth.

'May I join you?' Rose asks, suddenly awkward.

The chef pulls out the chair opposite John, but Rose waits for John's acquiescence. It comes with strangely old-fashioned gestures, an elegant sweep of the hand, a slight bow of the head.

'Detective Inspector,' he says. 'May I offer you a drink?'

Rose places the plastic bottle of Irn-Bru on the table.

The chef frowns. 'Will you be eating with us?'

The crisps and Twix have lost their appeal. 'Have you ordered?' she asks John.

'Aye.'

She turns to the chef. 'I'll have what he's having.'

She waits until the chef leaves before cutting to the chase. 'You didn't leave a phone number.'

He shrugs. 'Detective Inspector, what brings you here?'

She explains.

It took a couple of days for the police to track down Tall Willy. They were unable to interview him, as he had recently embarked on an extended trip through China by motorbike. His grandson sent them a link to his posts on social media. On the day the body was found in the old factory, William Hamish Angus MacDonald was alive and well, inspecting the undercarriage of a steam engine in Harbin.

The *primo piatto* arrives, *spaghetti alle vongole*. John watches as Detector Inspector Rose Irvine moves the food around, takes a suspicious bite, then wolfs it down. Giuseppe winks at John when he brings the Irn-Bru back in a decanter. The bright orange liquid contrasts nicely with the straw-coloured quarter carafe of *verdicchio* for John.

John doesn't touch his white wine until the fish arrives. Rainbow trout with almonds, melted butter and lemon in a silver sauce-boat.

Rose's eyes widen. 'You eat like this every day?'

'Aye.'

Cereal for breakfast, sandwich for tea. Since his wife died, just one hot meal a day on weekdays. Whatever his good friend Giuseppe recommends.

Not wishing to spoil her enjoyment of the tiramisu – she eats dessert, which he never does – he waits until their plates are tidied away and coffee is served before asking her about the autopsy.

'I need you to come back to the station,' Rose says.

'Now?'

The detective inspector checks her watch and frowns. 'Tomorrow.'

'The morn's morn.' He nods. 'I'll be there.'

Rose leaves first. She pays for her food, ignoring John's protests, and walks back to the car. The sun has burned through the haar. She peers though the window of Tesco Express. The checkout girl has been replaced by an older man.

In trouble again, is he?

What's he done this time?

Rose gets in her car and drives away.

Fifth Clue

BARBIE DOLL

NITRIC ACID – PLATINUM

Twenty

Barbie Doll

The detective inspector smells of lily-of-the-valley today. John watches the way she absent-mindedly strokes the hollow below her throat as she tells him the news.

The autopsy has been suspended. The corpse, preserved in several layers of hardened phosphate rock powder, was moved to a specialist forensic morgue. As the pathologist chipped through the carapace, the contents began to liquefy. After confirming the presence of human remains by chemical analysis, they sealed the shell and its grisly, deliquescent contents.

John is aware that she is watching his reaction.

He controls it carefully, unsettled by a new sense that she distrusts him. What has changed?

'Here.' She plonks a thick dossier on the table. Motes of dust dance in the February sunlight.

'Perhaps you saw one of this lot hanging around the factory.'

John shrugs. City docks are a magnet for misfits: those who work there, legally and illegally, and those who are lost.

'One of this lot?'

'Reported missing, never found.'

So, in the absence of forensic clues, the police are hoping that the body in the phosphate cave was that of a vagrant, a tramp, a runaway.

'Mispers,' she adds.

He opens the dossier reluctantly, knowing what to expect. So many of the photos are of bairns with shy, smiling faces. Little souls changed overnight by the rush of hormones, from sweet, docile children to angry, rebellious teenagers. Children who vanish, their families left in limbo, uncertain how to grieve – for their innocents who must surely have been abducted by evil hands unknown, or for their own failings as parents which led their offspring to run away and break all contact, or the worst combination of both.

Mispers.

Whispers.

But many of the names have no recent photo because no one cared enough to take one. Men and women of all ages released from institutions to 'care in the community', except there is no community which cares any more. Sleeping rough. Seeking warmth in cardboard and refuge in the needle or the bottle. Church meals at Christmas. In and out of hospital.

John turns the pages.

The clock ticks.

'Anyone look familiar?'

John shakes his head.

'You're sure? Take your time.'

He points to the tray. 'May I?'

She wrinkles her nose and then nods.

He reaches out to pick up the Barbie doll.

The plastic doll is nothing like a real woman: completely artificial, elongated and smooth. No scent, no warmth, no softness, no quiet breath. There is something disturbing about the sterile, silent plastic.

John runs his fingers over the naked form of the doll, looking for the scratches. Yes, this is it. The same one. He remembers undressing her. Slowly, carefully – as gently as his big, clumsy fingers would allow. He sighs when his fingernail finds the deep indentation on the small of the doll's back. At the squeal of a chair pushing back, he looks up. The detective inspector has moved away from him; he notes her discomfort and blushes.

'The missing catalyst,' he says by way of explanation, putting the doll back on the table and withdrawing his hands lest she mistake the checking for fondling.

'The catalyst for what?' Her eyes remain narrowed, the pupils glittering with suspicion and distaste, as if he is some sort of pervert.

'Nitric acid,' he says.

Twenty-one

Nitric Acid

Aqua fortis. Spirit of nitre. A clear, colourless liquid that turns pale yellow in air, giving off choking, reddish-brown fumes. Nasty stuff. Highly reactive. Useful for all the reasons that make it so dangerous.

It is one thing to know what something is made of, another thing to know how to make it. You might look at the formula for nitric acid, HNO_3 – one hydrogen, one nitrogen and three oxygens – and think it straightforward. Nitrogen and oxygen from the air, hydrogen from water. But knowing where you want to go and finding the best route to get there are different things.

If you want to go to New York from Leith, you could walk to Stranraer, row across the Irish Sea, squelch across Ireland and then swim the Atlantic. It might take some time, so you don't take the obvious route. Instead, you take the tram to Edinburgh Airport, where you might find that the cheapest option is far from direct – for example flying east to Amsterdam and then west to Detroit and then finally east again to the Big Apple.

But imagine you are taking the Scottish Youth Orchestra to play in Carnegie Hall, 120 teenagers with timpani and tubas and double basses. The route you choose might be different again.

So, it is one thing to know where you want to go, but quite another to get there at large scale and acceptable cost in a reasonable time. The skill in chemistry is finding the right stopping-off points to make the overall process economic, and here's where we must thank Mr Fritz Haber and Mr Wilhelm Ostwald[xix].

We've already met Mr Haber[xxi] with his high-temperature, high-pressure ammonia process. Mr Ostwald is less well-known, although he won a Nobel Prize for chemistry nine years before Mr Haber: in 1909 to be precise.

Latvian Willy, as John would have called him, was an interesting chap: a perpetual student, locked in conflict with his industrialist father who wanted him to join the family business making chemicals. One of those kids who already knows he is better than those around him at school, he probably didn't endear himself to his first professors by demonstrating that he was smarter than them too. Latvian Willy was more interested in chemistry than popularity; his single-mindedness was rewarded.

In Latvian Willy's process[E], ammonia reacts with oxygen to give nitric acid and water.

All very straightforward you might say. I could have thought of that. $NH_3 + O_2 = HNO_3 + H_2O$ Chemistry as anagrams; you just shift the letters around.

Except that I didn't tell you the secret ingredient. Nitrogen doesn't want to pair up with oxygen, it is happily bonded to hydrogen. You need to excite them both to get interest. Heat to a high temperature. Now the bonds start to weaken. The atoms spend more time apart. Even then, they remain bonded, faithful. If you were to remove the heat, they would unite again as if nothing had happened. So you force them into close proximity with others in the most dangerous and seductive situation, in a place where the normal rules don't apply. A catalyst. The finest bed of shiny metal gauze. A metal so precious it is indispensable to the wealth and health of the modern world.

Not only is platinum rare, but it is difficult to extract. Formed in dying stars and arriving on the earth in asteroids, it is found deep inside the Transvaal basin of South Africa. In the Bushveld Igneous Complex, mines like Amandelbult, Rustenberg, Marikana, Kroondal, Limpopo and Modikwa sink shafts deep into the ancient igneous intrusions. The miners go two kilometres underground and remove twenty thousand tonnes of dull grey bed rock for every twenty tonnes of ore, to find just one ounce[35] of platinum.

The rock is crushed in enormous mills. The noise is deafening, as thousands of hardened metal balls whizz around, crashing and banging and rattling, transferring the energy from the electric motors to the rock, which fractures on collision. The fine powder is poured into a huge jacuzzi, a flotation tank containing water and industrial bubble bath. Air is bubbled through the tub. The base rock falls to the bottom, but the metal-rich salts cling to the bubbles and dance. Rich in copper, nickel, platinum, palladium, ruthenium, rhodium, gold and silver, they pirouette to the surface and are skimmed off the top.

This concentrate is dried and heated in a smelter at temperatures of over one thousand degrees centigrade. It is treated to remove iron and sulphur, and then sent for refining, where each precious metal is separated by more clever chemistry.

First the base metals are removed: copper, nickel and cobalt. Then the precious metals: platinum, palladium, gold, rhodium, ruthenium, iridium, osmium, and silver. The platinum salt is a mustard-yellow powder when it is fed to the refinery. Platinum melts at 1,768 degrees centigrade and the liquid is poured into moulds, emerging as lustrous silvery-grey ingots of pure metal.

Platinum is used in healthcare: spinal surgery, pacemakers and stents. In cars: from fibreglass casings to catalytic converters. In energy: fuel cells and electrodes. It's used as a catalyst in the chemical and petrochemical industry, and for jewellery.

All that rock to be shifted, all those processing steps to carry out, the rarity of the metal and its value as a catalyst, means that platinum is expensive.

Very expensive.

Twenty-two

Platinum

The day they realised the true value of the missing platinum, John was the first person to be called into the investigation.

He had been on shift the day the man from the catalyst company unpacked the gauzes from the Securicor van. He watched in awe as the lustrous silvery tissue was unpeeled from a roll and placed gently, one layer on top of the other, onto a grid and trimmed to size. When the fitting was complete, the reactor for the new nitric acid plant was closed up, the job was signed off and the spare bits of gauze and sweepings were weighed and noted and returned to the stores to await secure shipment back to the supplier.

It wasn't until the package arrived back in Royston that they noticed the discrepancy in weight. Between leaving the area around the nitric acid reactor and arriving for packing at the factory store, a quantity had gone missing. The catalyst engineer checked his records and was able to identify the missing weight.

A triangular offcut of platinum gauze, the size of a large neckerchief, was missing.

Only one conclusion.

Theft.

There were many possible thieves.

Big Stu was the obvious culprit. An experienced fence, the leading hand's main income came from trading whisky stolen from the bonded warehouse that adjoined the Sally Street packing line. He had other interests, gold and silver of dubious origin, but John would not put it past him to diversify. However, Big Stu had been in Ibiza in the fortnight before the nitric acid plant started up.

John interrogated everyone who had been in attendance the day the catalyst was loaded. He had a sixth sense for the truth, and none of the operators or craftsmen gave him the slightest hint of deception. They appeared to be as flummoxed as everyone else.

John extended his inquiry to others on site that day, including the day shift. Becksy was well known for hoarding things as broken as himself. Half idiot, half magpie, the profoundly deaf greaser had a treasure trove of trash, and a knack for fixing things. Unlike Big Stu, Becksy was incapable of lying. When John confronted him, his sign language was eloquent. And it led him to the last person John would ever have suspected. The giant bulldozer driver: Brodie.

Brodie's biceps were the same circumference as his wife's waist. They used her dressmakers' tape to compare.

He worked on the farm with his father and grandfather. He also had a part share in a fishing trawler and sailed with it whenever his shift pattern matched the tide. The twelve hours that he spent shovelling at the factory were a relaxation compared to catching herring.

Brodie was wise about many things. About the weather, about the sea, about tractors. He could strip and rebuild a large engine, although his huge fingers sometimes had trouble with the smaller pieces. But he hated school. Rather than doing his homework at the long kitchen table in the evenings, he preferred to help his grandmother. She had a gift with pastry – puff pastry for beef wellington, fish pie, prawn *vol-au-vents*, sausage rolls; cold water pastry for game pie; shortcrust pastry for bramble and apple tart. When she passed away, he took over the cooking and surpassed her skill. Strong arms, cold hands and the warmest heart in Midlothian.

The farm grew winter wheat, kale and potatoes. Brodie learned the value of applied science a few years after he left school. The year that they couldn't afford fertiliser signalled the start of a downward spiral. Low yield, no money for good seed. The following year the yield was even lower. The family let the hired hands go and worked longer hours.

Brodie was walking past the local pub when the fertiliser salesman was thrown out. He recognised the man who gave sweets to the farm children when he visited. Brodie helped him to his feet and dusted him down. On hearing what had happened, he linked his sinewy, tartan-shirted arm with the thin one of the man in a suit and took him back inside. The men propping up the bar stopped laughing when Brodie walked in. He ordered a Babycham for the salesman and one for himself. This time, the bartender served it up instead of laughing. The men who had thrown the salesman out for requesting a bufty brew slunk away.

They talked. The salesman asked why Brodie's farm had stopped buying from him. Brodie, light-headed from the bubbles, outlined the farm's predicament. The salesman was shocked. Brodie's grandfather had told him that he was no longer welcome on the premises, too proud to tell him the real reason. He'd come to the local pub to try to find out more.

He explained to Brodie about the swap scheme: take the seed and fertiliser now and pay back an agreed percentage of the crop. The risk and rewards were shared. Brodie arranged to meet him with his father and grandfather the next day. A deal was struck. They never looked back.

The farm expanded. Brodie married a girl from a neighbouring farm. She was well-suited to the life of a farmer's wife, hard-working and frugal. She made all her own clothes and sewed dresses for dolls to bring in extra money. An avid reader, she was happy to read aloud when he lost his glasses or write things down for him if he had a sore hand.

When they needed an injection of cash for more machinery, Brodie called the fertiliser salesman for advice. Banks were reluctant to lend to farming families unless at least one member could show a steady income, so Brodie took the salesman's advice and applied for a shift job at the fertiliser factory. Brodie's wife filled in the application form, and he got the job.

Brodie was amazed by the factory. He'd imagined cutting-edge technology. But the granulation plant, where he now worked between farm and trawler, was just a huge mixer into which they shovelled all sorts of stuff and hoped for the best. On the premium grades, any product that didn't quite make the specification was diverted away from the conveyor that connected the production plant to the packing line in Sally Street. The reject gathered in growing mountains in the whalebone sheds of Leith waiting to be shovelled back into more forgiving grades of fertiliser with wider tolerance on the ratio of nitrogen, phosphorus and potash. Along with the odd bit of crap.

He told his wife about the new French design, which added a series of external boxers round a flexible chute prone to blockage: short thick shafts with rounded ends that pulled back slowly and then lunged forward to thump the soft rubber chute. When he demonstrated the exact motion to his wife at home at night, in the privacy of their bedroom, she enjoyed the practical demonstration just as much as he did.

Brodie had never tasted Babycham before rescuing the salesman who, in turn, rescued him. It is a bubbly sweet perry cider, a poor man's champagne. From that day, on the rare occasions that he drank alcohol, Babycham was the only drink that he ever ordered.

When he wasn't working, Brodie preferred the farmhouse kitchen to the pub. His wife's quiet company, seated by the Rayburn stove, needle in hand, while his bread dough rose, was all the relaxation he needed.

He liked to see her eyes light up when he brought her little gifts from the farm or the sea or the fertiliser factory: a sprig of young heather for a doll's corsage, tiny pearly shells for buttons, a scrap of strange, metallic, shimmering gauze for a dress. No wife was better loved; no dolls better dressed.

John struck a deal. He persuaded the investigating team not to treat the missing platinum as a theft until they first offered an amnesty. He was persuasive in suggesting that if someone had picked up a piece of pretty gauze without realising its value, they might just as likely return it if no questions were asked.

When the amnesty was announced, Brodie agonised for a while, but he knew that John was a man of his word. He arranged to meet him in the phosphate rock shed. When John appeared in the doorway, Brodie climbed down nervously from the bulldozer. They walked silently to his locker and he took out a plastic bag.

Inside was a Barbie doll. The ballroom style dress that Brodie's wife had made for the doll was a work of art. The lustrous ghostly silver glowed under the dim sodium lights of the raw material sheds. It was worth more than Brodie's annual salary.

John clapped Brodie on his broad back and his shoulders lost their uncharacteristic hunch and sprang back to ramrod straight. The two men exchanged no words during the whole meeting, but both understood perfectly.

Back in his office, John removed the valuable dress from the Barbie doll. Although he was careful, stray wires from the platinum gauze scratched the soft plastic in places, leaving deep indentations. He put the doll aside to give it to Polly for her daughter when the next phosphate boat came in.

He returned the platinum gauze in the form of a tiny dress to Wee Willy. The deputy works manager asked him many questions, but John's lips were sealed.

John informs the detective that the Barbie doll once wore a ball gown made of platinum gauze valued at £5,000. He suggests that they check the exact date of the last platinum sale to the Leith nitric acid plant from Johnson Matthey in Royston – but he hazards a guess that it was early in 1986. 'Where did the doll come from?' she asks.

John purses his lips and shakes his head.

Even now, he will not reveal his source.

An amnesty is an amnesty.

A promise is a promise.

Sixth Clue

NUTMEG GRATER

PHOSPHORIC ACID

Twenty-three

Nutmeg Grater

Inside the police interview room, the panes of glass are rattling in their frames. Through the high window, John can make out dark clouds scudding across the sky. Snow clouds perhaps. February often brings sleet and hail, although snow is uncommon in Edinburgh. It falls on the hills, rarely lying for long near the sea.

After retirement, he often sat out the winter in southern Spain, a three-month package costing considerably less than heating his flat. Benidorm isn't the same since his wife died. Now the February wind cuts him to the heart as well as to the bone.

'Did you recognise any of the mispers?'

'Can I look at the photos again?' John asks.

'Take your time.'

John pushes away the dossier of missing persons.

'Not these. The photos from the factory.'.

'The crime scene?'

'Aye.'

She picks up the phone and a few minutes later there is a knock at the door and a delivery.

'Thank you.' He nods at the constable.

'You're welcome.' She smiles back.

He flicks through the photographs and chooses one showing the objects on the table. Although they are covered in dust, John can still make out the shape of an elephant, a doll, a keyring, an air horn in the picture. He stands and starts to move the physical objects around on the tray.

'What are you doing?' she asks.

'Putting them back as they were found.'

'Why?'

He doesn't answer. He's not quite sure himself. It's important, but he lacks the words to explain.

He stands back to survey his handiwork.

'Can I see a list of factory employees?'

'You think the deceased might have worked at the factory?' asks the detective inspector. 'Why?'

John looks back at the photo of the crime scene, the position of the objects before recovery. The objects on the tray are now in the correct order. He didn't need the photo after all. It is the only order that makes sense.

'Gut feel,' he says.

He knows that she knows that there's more to this than he's telling her.

Perhaps he owes her an explanation.

He picks up a hollow metal object, a square-based pyramid narrowing to a circular opening at the top, the whole thing about the size of John's fist. At the base, a little plastic drawer slides out, opening and closing smoothly with the aid of a plastic knob. At the top, a hooped handle allows the user to steady the equipment during operation or hang it up for show. One side has fine indentations, star-shaped holes with sharp edges, as if tiny bullets had been fired out at regular intervals from the inside. On the opposite side the holes are larger, elongated openings each with a sharp lip. It is a miniature kitchen grater, common enough in the middle-class homes of Edinburgh, up and down Heriot Row and India Street, Royal Circus and Moray Place. The amateur MasterChefs of Edinburgh were probably grating nutmeg or lemon zest with exactly such an object right now. Not so common in a factory in Leith.

There's only one person this could belong to.

Twenty-four

Fitting In

The trouble with Fraser was his education. He'd been in his first year at university when his girlfriend fell pregnant. 'Fell' made it sound as if he had nothing to do with it, but maybe she'd fallen because he'd pushed.

He'd thought that he loved her once. Before he started university and discovered that he preferred intelligent conversation to fawning adoration. She was his first, and he might never have known better if she had been his only lover, but freshers' week quickened his pulse and opened his eyes to possibilities. He had adventures. He made friends. With women even. He fell in love with a girl from Manchester. He was going to tell his first girlfriend. And then she told him.

Both families agreed that Fraser must marry and get a job. Times were hard, but his uncle was in the lodge and pulled a few favours. Before long Fraser had dropped out of university to work shifts on a phosphoric acid plant in a fertiliser factory beside the North Sea.

Most of the shift workers had fought hard to get a job at the factory. The rules were clear. The pay was fair. The pension was excellent. Those injured at work were given desk jobs, like Blind Willy in the gatehouse. Few left voluntarily.

But for Fraser, it was the pits, the bottom of the barrel, the death of his dreams. He was young and self-absorbed, unaware of the contempt that shone out in his slow walk, the fastidious dislike written on his hunched shoulders. No one doubted that he was bright. He learned to operate the plants quickly and resented the fact that he was given the menial outside jobs when the older men sat clueless at the control panel. Initially he took pride in his shift logs, clear firm handwriting full of accurate and precise information. But no one else could understand the words he used, they thought that he was mocking them. Before long he had adopted the factory slang. U/S for useless, knackered, broken. Just like him.

There were two phosphoric acid operators on John's shift, Hughie and Fraser. Hughie, the panel man, spent his shift with his feet up in a warm control room reading a magazine: Playboy or Rustler.

Fraser, who had briefly studied English Literature at university, found work to do outside. To say that the two men didn't get on would be an understatement.

John treated Fraser exactly the same as any other member of his shift team. He knew that the lad didn't drink, but still insisted on his morning or evening 'kiss'. He saw that the boy was young and strong but unused to hard physical work, so he gave him extra tasks to toughen him up. He offered regular advice on how to fit in.

Fraser ignored John's advice.

But he did learn how to operate a phosphoric acid plant.

Twenty-five

Phosphoric Acid

Phosphoric acid is made by reacting phosphate rock with a strong acid[C]. Hydrogen from sulphuric acid swaps places with calcium in the rock, giving solid calcium sulphate, which is known as gypsum, and liquid phosphoric acid. A filter then separates the solids from the liquid.

The reaction is easy. But the trick to making phosphoric acid is good filtration, and the trick to good filtration is crystallisation. Large, well-formed crystals with even shape and size allow the liquid to drain easily. Unfortunately, calcium sulphate crystals come in several shapes and sizes: a mixture of awkward needle-shaped crystals, rhomboid lozenges, x-shaped swallowtail twins and thin flat plates. Small crystals plug the gaps between large crystals, tiny crystals get in-between, blocking the filter cloth, and before long the liquid has nowhere to go. The reaction conditions determine the crystal structure of the gypsum which in turn determines the ease of filtration.

After establishing the ideal reaction conditions to make good crystals, you still have to separate the solid from the liquid.

There are many types of filter for continuous processes, but the tilting pan Prayon filter is a mechanical work of art.

Imagine a huge clock face, the diameter of four tall men lying head to toe. Imagine that inside the fixed clock face is a giant rotating bicycle wheel, divided into twelve segments by spokes. Each of the segments is filled with tea strainers. Now imagine that the huge bicycle wheel is rotating slowly. At twelve o'clock there is a teapot, constantly pouring a mixture of freshly brewed tea and tea leaves onto the segment as it passes underneath. As the strainers move round, the strong tea drains through and only the damp tea leaves are left. At six o'clock there is a kettle, constantly pouring hot water onto the damp tea leaves to make weak tea, which is collected before nine o'clock and poured back over the leaves at three o'clock

Underneath the turning tea strainers there are a series of collectors, cups, jugs, a vacuum cleaner, hairdryer and a dustbin.

Under one and two o'clock there is a porcelain cup: this is where the strong tea, the product, will collect. There is a blank under three o'clock where the weak tea is added to wash the tea leaves. Under four and five o'clock is a jug, where the weak tea will collect and be recycled back into the teapot. Under six there is a blank where the hot water is added. Under seven and eight there is a jug which will collect watery tea to be added back at three o'clock to make weak tea. Under nine and ten o'clock is the vacuum cleaner to suck the tea leaves dry. Under eleven o'clock is the bin. At this point the strainer is tipped upside down and a hairdryer blows through the bottom to push the dry, spent tea leaves into the waste. The strainer tips back and the process starts again.

If you keep adding dry tea leaves to the teapot, but fail to add more liquid, the tea leaves stay small, they don't stretch and swell and grow. The tea is strong, but there isn't enough of it, and lots of valuable flavour is left unextracted in the waste tea leaves.

If you add too much liquid, then the tea becomes weak and tasteless.

OK, so now replace the tea leaves with gypsum and the tea with phosphoric acid.

But don't drink it.

It's not a perfect analogy but at least you now understand counter-current filtration, and the importance of getting the process into a perfect balance.

At Leith, 70 per cent sulphuric acid was pumped through a pipe to the reactor: a large rubber-lined tank. The phosphate rock poured in from a conveyor belt and the reaction was controlled by the ratio of acid to rock. A recycle of weak phosphoric acid from the filter kept it at just the right concentration. Too strong and the wrong sort of crystals form. Too weak and they don't form at all.

When starting up in a clean vessel after a shutdown, the reaction had to be seeded by the plant manager, who would throw in a handful of gypsum to get things started.

The reactor would fill slowly with acid and rock, with regular samples taken to the factory lab. Long before the reactor reached its operating level, it would start to feed the filter, but with all the liquid produced recycled straight back to the reactor instead of being exported as product. Once the reaction conditions were established, perfect crystals forming in the reactor, the feed into the reactor was adjusted to balance the feed out to the filter and the export of phosphoric acid began.

After the gypsum was removed by filtration, the phosphoric acid was concentrated in a huge evaporator. The acid became more aggressive as it got hotter, so to keep the cost of construction materials down, the boiling point was lowered.

Water was removed under vacuum created by huge steam ejectors and condensed by sea water.

The process ran continuously, seven days a week, twenty-four hours a day, all by itself. With a little help from the phosphoric acid plant operators.

Twenty-six

Crystals

Hughie had no idea that his job was to grow crystals. As far as he was concerned, gypsum was rubbish that got dumped out to sea. His job was to make phosphoric acid. A job that would have been easier if he didn't have to work with Fraser.

One night, Hughie was so annoyed by Fraser's use of peculiar words that he had to telephone the granulation plant operator to vent. He didn't notice something was wrong until an alarm interrupted his conversation.

He looked up at the panel. The flow from the reactor to the rotating filter had stopped.

He checked the reactor level. Without any flow out and with feeds continuing in, the reactor level was rising fast. Hughie took immediate action. He stopped the wash water flow to the filter, the recycle acid and the sulphuric acid feeds to the reactor.

Then he called Fraser.

Why didn't Hughie stop the phosphate rock?

Liquid feeds are easy to stop and start. You press a big red button on a control panel, and an automatic valve closes. When you want to start it up again, you press a smaller green button, the valve opens and Bob's your uncle. Or at least, Hughie thought sourly, Bob was Fraser's uncle, which was the only reason the posh git had a job.

Solids are messy things. Miles of conveyor belts trundled through overhead gantries to ferry the phosphate rock from a whalebone shed to the reactor. Although it was possible to press an emergency button in the control room to stop the final belt, there was no way to restart the solid feed from the control room. When the final belt tripped, it took time for the other belts to stop. Sometimes that led to a pile up, mountains of powdered rock spilling over motors and gears and sprockets. Each belt had to be checked, sometimes shovelled clear, before each belt motor could be restarted, and that meant climbing up to the gantry and walking miles with a shovel to check, clear and restart each belt in turn.

During the daytime, he could leave it to Fraser to request assistance from one of the greasers, but at night there was only Hughie and Fraser and restarting the phosphate rock feed was a two-man job.

So Hughie left it running.

When Fraser appeared, expecting to be given another menial task, some new humiliation to be heaped on top of the last, he was spoiling for another verbal battle. Hughie took the wind out of his sails by asking him for help to find the fault and restart the flow to the filter. It took a while, but fault-finding was what Fraser was good at.

Fraser traced the pipe between the reactor and filter. All the valves were open, nothing visually amiss. He laid hands on the pipe wherever it was accessible until he detected a cold spot, in the S-bend after a long straight run. The ideal place for some sticky gypsum to settle out, a plug made of plaster of Paris. He went to the stores and withdrew a steam hose and a mallet and set to work to clear the blockage. Within the hour, the slurry was flowing to the filter again.

John always checked the shift production volume, so when Fraser got the flow back to the filter, Hughie exported the phosphoric acid to the storage tanks, strong and weak, all of it: he didn't bother sending any recycle back to the reactor for another hour. Just to catch back up.

He restarted the liquid flows, put his feet up and opened a magazine.

Fraser returned the steam hose and mallet to the stores and wandered up onto the filter floor. He stood for a while watching the tilting pan filter. Something was wrong. The first hint of trouble was the sound of slopping liquid, a squelch from the pans as they tilted. The pale golden powder, easily dislodged by a pulse of compressed air to the underside, was being replaced by a brown slurry.

The liquid wasn't passing cleanly through the solid, some remained lying on top of it. The export rate of phosphoric acid began to fall. As things went from bad to worse, more liquid began to splash over the sides of the filter instead of passing through.

Fraser rapped on the window of the control room.

Rat-a-tat-tap.

Hughie took one look at the overflowing filter and pressed a button to stop the wash water. He checked the reactor level. Fraser had restarted the flow out of the reactor just in time, but the level was still too high. If it continued rising, the very high level would trip the reactor feeds and they would spend the rest of the shift shovelling phosphate rock.

Hughie knew what to do; he had done it many times before. He got out the long sharp knife he kept in his locker for these occasions. He lashed it to the end of the extra-long broom handle, the brush that John had provided for sweeping down the phosphate rock where it settled on the overhead ducts, the one that Hughie never used for its intended purpose.

Hughie showed Fraser how to make cuts in the filter cloth

as each empty pan came around to twelve o'clock. The effect was dramatic. Finding an easier path, the liquid stopped slopping over the side and found its way back into the process. Hughie restarted the water washing, the recycle of liquid to the reactor re-established itself and by the end of the shift beautiful crystals were growing again.

Fraser was impressed, but made the mistake of writing a vivid and detailed description of the solution to the problem in his handover log.

As a result the plant manager finally understood the mysterious and regular failure of the filter cloths which led to the silting up of the vacuum system, the furring of the product pipes with gypsum, the downtime to change filter cloths and overhaul the vacuum system and the resulting overspend on his maintenance budget.

When Hughie stopped the acid feed to the reactor, the concentration of solids increased, lots of tiny crystals of gypsum emerged instead of a smaller number of large ones. When Hughie stopped the filter wash and recycle, even less liquid was collected for recycle and the mixture in the reactor became thicker and thicker and increasingly difficult to filter.

After he'd disciplined Hughie (and for the sake of fairness, Fraser as well) the plant manager explained to all the operators that if they ever had filtration problems like that again, the only way to solve it was to lower the solids concentration in the reactor: stop the phosphate rock conveyors and add water to the reactor until the concentration is back to normal. He wrote a beautiful and clear procedure which only Fraser read.

From Hughie's point of view, if you have a choice between:

A. Stopping all feeds to the reactor, ringing John to get the stores key, searching the stores for a long water hose, inspecting it for damage, lugging it half a mile down icy roads, connecting one end to the tap on the edge of the sulphuric acid plant, hauling the length three stories up over the tanks and connecting the other end to the phosphoric acid reactor, going back down to turn on the water, taking regular samples to perform an acid base titration until the concentration is right, walking through miles of dimly lit tunnel to check, clean and restart each of the five long phosphate rock conveyor belts in turn and then restarting the other feeds

and

B. slitting a few filter cloths with a sharp knife on a long pole from the warmth of the operating floor

which would you choose on a freezing winter night?

Hughie didn't bother to read the new procedure, but he understood that it was time to alter his cloth-ripping technique to make it undetectable. The trouble was Fraser: how to stop him snitching? Something had to be done about Fraser.

Fraser, his new wife and bairn moved in with his parents while he saved up the deposit on a place of their own. His mother felt sorry for her darling son and went to special lengths to provide him with a decent meal when the canteen wasn't open at work.

After being unfairly disciplined for something Hughie had done, Fraser became more morose than ever. Fraser's mum could see that he was low, so she packed a special tea for his bait on Saturday night shift: a Marks and Spencer's ready meal of pasta in a creamy seafood sauce. Serves two. And a bag of ready washed Italian salad with rocket and radicchio. She even added a little pot of olive oil and wine vinegar dressing, a chunk of Parmesan and her tiny nutmeg grater.

When Hughie got his meat pie from the oven and saw what Fraser was about to put in, he went back to the control room and called John.

Fraser was sitting at the Formica table, with a book open beside him (*Middlemarch* by George Eliot) when John appeared and fished in the bin. He sat down next to Fraser. Without saying a word, he laid out his trawl. He smoothed out the cellophane bag with a picture of salad, wiped a drip of creamy sauce from the cardboard sleeve revealing the picture of prawns and mussels on a bed of green *tagliatelle*, sniffed at the contents of the little glass pot and picked up the tiny grater, holding it up to the light to inspect the crumbs of Parmesan trapped in the zester.

John started to laugh. Fraser looked surprised. He blushed, tried to ignore the noise and continue eating. The laugh lasted many long minutes until Fraser picked up his half-eaten tea, put it in the bin and walked out.

Fraser told his mum that he would make his own bait in future.

The wind is getting louder, howling like a banshee. In the police interview room, John places the nutmeg grater carefully back on the tray. The detective inspector leans forward to inspect it.

'You recognise this?' she asks. 'Know who it belonged to?'
'Aye.'

The clock ticks.

Rose waits.

'He didn't fit in, you see,' John says.

Rose leans forward. 'Who didn't fit in?'

'Fraser.' John tells her the story of Fraser's offensively posh bait. He doesn't mention the incident that came later, the time they changed the seawater screens. He can't bear to think about that.

'Weren't you a little hard on the lad?' She crosses her arms. 'Who cares what he ate?'

'You don't understand.' John shakes his head. 'When you're new, your first job is to fit in. You have to earn the right to be different. That comes later, years later.'

Rose raises her eyebrows and shrugs. 'So what happened to Fraser?'

After the seawater screen incident, Fraser didn't come back to work.

'He left,' John said. 'Quite suddenly.'

'He resigned?'

'Nope. No warning. One shift, he just didn't turn up.'

'When was this?'

'February 1987.'

She stares at him. 'How can you be so sure of the date?'

John frowns. Because of Polly, of course. It was not the sort of thing a man forgets.

The clock ticks.

'It was a hard winter,' he says.

A little shiver passes through her. She sighs before continuing. 'Did anyone try to contact him?'

'Mebbie.' Nobody from John's shift, that was for sure. They were all glad to see the back of the supercilious bugger. HR might have tracked him down, but they were tight-lipped with information. 'Not that anyone told me.' Everyone just assumed he couldn't hack it, couldn't face them again, had gone back to university or found another job. No one minded too much; there was plenty of overtime until he was replaced.

Rose leans forward, eyes sparkling. 'What if he never left?'

John scratches his head. He wouldn't put it past Hughie to murder the lad. Although the staging makes no sense, and it is hard to imagine someone as lazy as Hughie lugging a body all the way from the phosphoric acid plant, through miles of tunnels to the phosphate rock intake. Brodie has the strength, but Brodie wouldn't hurt a fly.

Rose stands up. 'I think we'd better check this out.'

Seventh Clue

SUNGLASSES

SULPHURIC ACID

Twenty-seven

Broken Sunglasses

In the police interview room, John provides a young constable with a detailed description of Fraser Docherty, erstwhile operator of the phosphoric acid plant at the Leith Fertiliser Works: a good-looking lad, nice physique, five foot ten inches or so, clean-shaven with short dark hair and blue eyes. In his early twenties when he started at the factory in 1983, he always wore funny clothes – pointy shoes with zips, drainpipe trousers with rips, PVC raincoat. Unhappily married to a lass called Moira who had an uncle in the lodge by the name of Robert, Fraser was last seen in February 1987.

When the constable finishes her notes, Rose stands up, dusting down her uniform as if stray words of his have stuck and need to be removed.

'Lunchtime?' John suggests, with a nod to the ticking clock.

The passing of the hours and story of the seafood *tagliatelle* with Parmesan and dressed salad has made John hungry. Times have changed. He has changed. He relishes the sort of food that he would have spurned before.

'Can we take a break?' He hopes that she cannot hear his stomach noises, embarrassing fizzing and gurgling from under the table.

'Not today,' she says.

Detective Inspector Rose Irvine asks John to remain seated while they check the records on Fraser Docherty.

'I can send out for a sandwich...' the young constable offers, faltering under Rose's hard stare.

'Egg mayonnaise,' John says. 'Thanks, doll.' He reaches into his pocket for some coins.

'Check on Fraser Docherty first.' Rose interrupts. 'It shouldn't take long.' She sniffs, as if to tell him it's a rotten lead.

He tends to agree. Fraser might have abandoned his young wife and bairn, quarrelled with her parents, his parents, cut off all contact with them and the uncle in the lodge. But Fraser's not on the misper list. And a nice boy like that would be missed if he disappeared out of the blue.

Not like the rest of them.

Poor buggers.

A different uniform brings him a limp cheese sandwich and a lukewarm cup of tea. John thanks him and eats it slowly as he wonders about Rose's new coldness. He closes his eyes for a few minutes.

When he opens them again, the clock has moved on. He pushes the misper dossier out of sight and turns his attention to the remaining items on the tray.

The sunglasses are the wrap-around type. John recognises them immediately by the shape of the fracture where they snapped. Right between the eyes.

He grasps the two halves by the legs. Opaque. Peering up through the dark lenses at the ceiling of the police station interview room, the harsh fluorescent tubes disappear. Useful glasses if you ever get invited to a Dan Flavin exhibition.

John stands and moves to the window. Winter sun in Edinburgh has a special quality. So special they only unwrap the Turner watercolours, held in pitch dark in the basement

136

of the National Museum of Scotland, in January and show them for twenty-nine days (January the first and second being important holidays for the Scots to nurse Hogmanay hangovers) when the light is as weak and watery as the pictures. But by February it is fiercer, hanging low in the sky and sending out razor-sharp shafts of icy cold light. With the glasses on, even the sun disappears, leaving only a faint corona around the edge of the lenses.

John closes his eyes and tries to imagine what it's like to go blind.

Twenty-eight

Sulphuric Acid

The hazards of oil of vitriol had been known for at least twelve hundred years before the acid deprived Willy of his sight. They said it was his own fault.

After the accident, Willy tended to agree with what anybody said.

They said that he had been a good operator. He ran the plant for twenty years before the accident. No one doubted that he understood the process.

So why did he do what he did?

The eighth-century alchemist Jabir ibn Hayyan[i] was the first to record production of sulphuric acid, calling it oil of vitriol.

In 1746, the British medical doctor and entrepreneur John Roebuck[v] started producing sulphuric acid in lead-lined wooden boxes. Improvements in equipment were made by others, including French chemist Joseph Louis Gay-Lussac[xi] and the lead chamber process was used until the British vinegar merchant Peregrine Phillips[xii] patented the more economical contact process in 1831.

In the contact process, sulphur, oxygen and water react to make sulphuric acid[B]. Of course, it's a little more complicated than that.

First, solid sulphur melts and is pumped to a chamber where it is burned with air to form sulphur dioxide[B1]. The same pungent gas is released by volcanoes. In tiny amounts it is a useful anti-microbial, and you'll find it in dried fruits, like apricots and sultanas. It goes by the alias of preservative E220.

The volcano gas is then reacted with further oxygen in the air to form sulphur trioxide[B2]. This is the gas responsible for acid rain. Tiny quantities of sulphur trioxide in the air react with water to form sulphuric acid. Fortunately for the marble statues and forests of this world, the oxidation of sulphur dioxide, SO_2, to sulphur trioxide, SO_3, is slow and difficult. In Willy's plant the trick to conversion was a catalyst.

A catalyst is something that promotes a chemical reaction without being directly involved. It can provide a site for reacting molecules to meet or a shortcut for their travel, a lower energy pathway. It remains unaltered while all around is change.

In the case of Willy's sulphuric acid plant, the catalyst was vanadium pentoxide. Thousands of star-shaped, yellow-orange pellets were loaded into the reactor.

Sulphur trioxide reacts violently with water, liberating a vast amount of heat. It's impractical and unsafe to react large volumes of sulphur trioxide with water. So, sulphur trioxide is gently absorbed into concentrated sulphuric acid to form a super-concentrated, fuming acid called oleum[B3].

Oleum is peculiar stuff. As the concentration increases, its properties change in unexpected ways. With a concentration of 20 per cent it freezes at minus ten degrees centigrade, but if it absorbs more sulphur trioxide, the freezing point rises to a maximum of fifteen degrees centigrade. Don't be fooled though. As it gets stronger again the freezing point falls to zero.

Oleum is viscous and surprisingly unreactive, to the point where it can be stored and transported in mild steel vessels and pipes. In a Scottish fertiliser plant, where the temperature outside can be lower than the freezing point, it is important to both keep the pipes and vessels warm and to get the concentration right.

The oleum is diluted with water to the concentration of acid required[B4]. Back to 98 per cent concentrated acid for recycling through the process to pick up further sulphur trioxide. Down to 70 per cent sulphuric acid to feed the phosphoric acid plant. Don't forget to change the materials of construction: rubber-lined vessels, stainless steel pipes. Sulphuric acid can cut through mild steel like a knife through butter.

The industrial contact process patented in 1831 is still in use today, although the expensive platinum catalyst favoured by the illustrious vinegar merchant is now replaced by the far more economic caesium-promoted vanadium pentoxide.

More sulphuric acid is produced each year than any other chemical, with two hundred and fifty million tonnes shipped globally in 2019. It is used in the production of iron and steel, paper, water treatment, electronics and medicines.

Unfortunately for Willy, it is also used in the production of fertiliser.

Twenty-nine

The Blinding

On the day of the accident, a hard frost had set in.

Willy was writing his log in the control room when an alarm sounded from the panel. He checked the readings and traced the problem back to a low flow of concentrated acid to the dilution plant.

Willy put on his donkey jacket, stepped outside and shivered. The pump was running, the motor whirring, the inlet and outlet valves wide open and yet the pressure gauge was reading zero, so it was not unnatural to assume, given the peculiar freezing point curve of oleum, that there might be a blockage in the pipe.

Willy did what any self-respecting process operator at the time would have done: he found a steam hose and a hammer.

When the pipe split and the concentrated sulphuric acid encountered Willy's eyes, the first burn was a chemical burn. The proteins and lipids in his living tissue were destroyed by amide and ester hydrolysis. The second burn was a thermal burn. The strong acid absorbed the moisture from his eyes, liberating heat. Willy couldn't distinguish the chemical burn from the thermal burn. All he could do was scream.

John heard the commotion from inside the shift manager's office. At first it was a howl of shock rather than pain: those cries would come later. John put down his mug of tea, dropped his half-eaten Tunnock's caramel wafer and ran towards the noise. He was second on the scene. Roger was already there;

he had pulled Willy to the safety shower and was holding him down. John took in the situation with one glance and walked swiftly past them to the sulphuric acid plant office. He calmly phoned Alec, the gateman, and told him to call an ambulance and declare an emergency in that order. He put on the rubber gloves that Willy kept in his donkey jacket and armed himself with the eyewash bottle from the lab. He shouted at Roger to hold on to Willy as he embraced them in the outdoor shower. Willy wouldn't open his eyes, so Roger had to pin him to the wall while John forced his eyelids apart to irrigate them. It was too late. The acid had attacked the cornea, and where his eyes had once been clear blue with dark pupils, they were now completely white and opaque.

They saved his life, however. Willy cursed them for that during months of pain in one hospital after another. His complete blindness spared him the awful sight of his scarred face and body. He could only feel the ridges of the scar tissue and the edges of the skin grafts with the pinkie of his left hand. His other fingertips, burned as he tried to remove his acid-soaked clothes, would never recover any feeling.

The investigation into what had happened focused on Willy's failure to follow procedure. He should not have hit the frozen oleum pipe with a hammer. Furthermore, if he was intent on clearing a blockage, he should have worn personal protective equipment; he definitely should not have approached the problem without goggles, a face shield, an acid suit, rubber boots and gloves. His unprotected eyes and flesh should not have been anywhere near when the pipe tore and the spray from a tsunami of concentrated sulphuric acid engulfed him.

Tall Willy was still supervising carpenters in Aberdeen at the time of the accident. Otherwise he might have inspected the torn pipe more closely and noticed a clean tear along the bottom, nowhere near where Willy had thwacked it, almost as if someone had taken a knife to butter. He would have measured the thickness of the mild steel pipe and seen that it was thick at the top and paper thin at the bottom.

He would have scratched his head, looked up and noticed the long red rubber hose that ran from the tank farm, up over the oleum piping to the phosphoric acid reactor. He might not have realised its critical contribution to optimising gypsum crystal growth, but he would have moved away because of the steady stream of water leaking from the hose where a sulphur lorry once ran over it. He would have marvelled at the bad luck that allowed the leak to be positioned so the water ran into the vent from the oleum pump pressure relief valve. He would have followed the slope of the vent pipe and realised that the water could have pooled in a section of pipe, reacted with the oleum to form dilute sulphuric acid and chomped through the mild steel in a matter of minutes.

He would have confirmed his thesis that there never was a blockage by stripping the pump and discovering that the impeller had completely corroded away. The pressure gauge showed zero not because it was U/S, but because there was no pressure.

The contract pipe fitter who replaced the section of piping between pump and absorber did report the shocking state of the horizontal sections of piping. He was told by his boss to shut up and get on with it. The boss wasn't all bad: he did help the crew move the bloody hose that was spraying water all over them as they worked.

The shift fitter who overhauled the oleum pump before the acid plant could restart was bemused as to where the impeller had gone. But no one read the shift fitter's report that he'd had to replace it, and no one thought to connect this fact to the accident.

Blind Willy took all the blame.

One year after the last of the skin grafts and two years after the accident, Blind Willy was back at work. His wife drove him in. Every morning she tidied his hair, prematurely white from the shock, and straightened his shirt collar. Every morning he stroked her face with the pinkie of his left hand, and she kissed his scarred face in return. She handed him his white stick as he got out of the car and waited patiently while he shuffled past the barrier, tapping to find the door to the gatehouse. She would not leave until she saw him seated at his chair in a spot that would catch the early morning sun. Alec would wave to her as he set down a cup of tea in front of Blind Willy, and then she would leave for the bakery where she worked.

Blind Willy was grateful that the bosses kept him on. He sat at the window of the gatehouse, answered the phone and operated a switchboard specially modified for him. The men saw his scars as they came in: the best safety campaign a factory ever had.

Blind Willy could not see, so he relied on what was left of his other senses. His sense of smell was not quite as developed as John's, but he still used it to monitor who was in the room. He recognised Big Alec by his halitosis, Hughie by the aftershave he wore, Brodie by the whiff of manure and herring that never quite washed off a farmer fisherman. Blind Willy's hearing was acute. He understood anxiety, pain, trepidation and depression and would offer proactive counsel to his colleagues in his soft Hebridean lilt. He suffered from the cold and liked to sit in the sun, but his eyes were highly sensitive. Light caused him pain, so he always wore special sunglasses to protect his eyes.

As the costs of transporting sulphur continued to climb, the men at head office calculated that they could import sulphuric acid more cheaply than making it. You might have thought Blind Willy would rejoice at the news, but he was gutted, every bit as upset as the other men, when the sulphur section closed. On the day of the announcement, he threw his glasses to the ground just as Becksy was walking towards him. The glasses snapped in two under the greaser's boot. Becksy was mortified, signalling his distress to Alec who ignored him and phoned for Blind Willy's wife to come and fetch her husband home.

John gave Blind Willy the little ebony elephant to distract him as he waited in the windowless telephone exchange. The injured gateman held the object in his palm, stroking the smooth surface with the pinkie of his left hand as tears rolled from blind eyes down scarred cheeks.

The body in the phosphate cave is not that of Blind Willy. John is sure of that. Blind Willy died peacefully in his bed within a few months of retirement. John attended his funeral at the crematorium.

So the little elephant must have been passed on to someone else. Someone who needed comfort even more than Blind Willy.

Eighth Clue

BRASS WASHER

AMMONIUM NITRATE

Thirty

Brass Washer

The clock has moved on when the detective inspector returns to the interview room.

'Any news?' John asks. 'Did you find Fraser Docherty?'

'We're working on it,' she says. 'What about the other things? Anything else here linked to Fraser?'

John surveys the remaining objects and shakes his head.

'Nope.'

She picks up a dull gold disc with a hole through the middle.

'Anyone else who suddenly vanished?' she asks.

John takes the metal ring from her and sniffs, hoping to retrieve the familiar pungent hit. Nothing. Not even a whiff. No trace of ammonia detectable.

A few years ago, John tried to buy ammonia from a high-street chemist, searching through the shelves, desperate for a quick hit to clear his cold. The pharmacist laughed at his request and offered him Olbas Oil or Fisherman's Friend Extra Strong Lozenges instead. Eucalyptus cleared his sinuses; menthol made his eyes water, but neither evoked the same memories.

He catches the detective staring at him and raises his nose from the brass washer.

No smell, but plenty for the eye to see. John holds the thick ring up to the light. He slips a pinkie into the centre and nods as fine green crystals tumble onto the desk.

Copper nitrate.

Just as he guessed.

John knows exactly where the washer has been, and who was responsible for the state it's in, but the commissioning disaster is a long story and he senses that Detective Inspector Rose Irvine is not in the mood.

He is rescued by a knock on the door.

Rose opens the door to the young constable. 'Any joy?'

'Not yet, we're waiting to speak with Mrs Docherty, his mam.' The constable's voice is barely a whisper and John has to strain to hear. 'But she's away on holiday.'

'Keep trying.'

'The boss wants a word.'

'Now?'

'Before the team meeting.'

Rose glances at the clock and sighs. She nods at John and points to the door. 'You'd better go,' she says. 'We don't need you here.'

Which is exactly what John had said to Keith.

Thirty-one

Ammonium Nitrate

Seven thousand miles south and west of Leith, the Atacama Desert sits on a plateau in the rain shadow of the Bolivian Southern Highlands, Peruvian Andes and Chilean Coastal Mountains. One of the driest places on earth, it is home to a huge deposit of sodium nitrate, once a valuable source of nitrates for fertiliser and explosives.

A dispute over this valuable resource led to the 1879–1884 'Saltpetre War' between Chile and a Bolivian–Peruvian alliance.

Chile won.

Now the desert is littered with abandoned mining towns – Chacabuco, Humberstone, Santa Laura, Puelma, and Oficina Anita – all shut down after the Haber-Bosch process for fixing nitrogen from the air led to the end of Chilean saltpetre exports.

In Botswana, six thousand miles from Leith, and from Chile, bat droppings in Drotsky's cavern have been transformed by bacteria over time into almost pure ammonium potassium nitrate. Named *gwihabaite* after the caves in which the mineral was found, these are the only known 'natural' sources of nitrates.

Thanks to our friends Fritz Haber and Karl Bosch, we are no longer reliant on Chilean saltpetre or fermented African bat poo to put back the nitrogen removed from the fields in our food. In fact, it was the Allied powers' blockade of shipments from Chile at the start of the First World War that sped up domestic production of ammonia, using nitrogen from the air in the Haber process.

In some countries, like the USA, a solution of ammonia is injected directly into the soil. But thanks to Wilhelm Ostwald and his process for turning ammonia into nitric acid, we can also make nitrogen salts.

Reacting ammonia with nitric acid (also made from ammonia) gives a white crystalline solid that is water soluble[F]. This ammonium nitrate packs the same amount of nitrogen in a granule of white fertiliser as there is butter in a croissant. It's a valuable fertiliser, popular in Scotland and sold under the trademark name of Nitram.

It takes a lot of ammonia to make ammonium nitrate – ammonia for the nitric acid and more ammonia to neutralise the acid. So when the decision was taken to double the capacity of the Nitram plant at Leith, a new ammonia line had to be built.

Thirty-two

Design

The great commissioning disaster began with the uprate to the ammonium nitrate plant.

The design of the new ammonia supply was entrusted to Keith, a contract mechanical engineer who could quote British Standards verbatim but avoided eye contact.

Keith was a tall, lean, distant man. In his early forties, he kept his curly brown hair short and his beard and moustache neatly clipped. He'd worked hard to progress from fitter's assistant to graduate engineer, proud to have pulled himself up by his bootstraps from humble beginnings, attending night classes then labouring to pay his way through university. He had a low opinion of the men who had once been his team-mates, and an exaggerated respect for design codes, level-five project plans, quality systems, contracts, performance indicators and compliance.

At the fertiliser factory, ammonia gas could go one of three ways. To be consumed by the granulation or Nitram plants as a small supplement to the main liquid feed, or to the refrigeration plant where it was cooled and returned to the storage spheres as liquid.

The amount of gas available varied. On a sunny summer day, too much gas formed when a warm rail tanker offloaded into the cold spheres. The refrigeration plant had to be run at full power and the rate of tanker discharge controlled. On winter nights, when the temperature fell below freezing, a compressor was required to push the liquid ammonia from the rail cars into storage and no surplus gas was available.

Both gas and liquid ammonia travelled in pipelines. The pipelines ran from storage spheres at the far north of the site, west to the Nitram plant or south to granulation. The pipes soared above the site as they crossed roadways and rail tracks, snaking across low utility buildings and around tall chimneys, kept out of harm's way by a pipe bridge, a set of steel girders on tall concrete supports.

Gas lines have to be much fatter than liquid lines to carry the same mass flowrate. A gas occupies more than a thousand times the volume of a liquid at the same temperature and pressure. You can reduce that volume by compressing the gas, applying Boyle's law[36], (see Robert Boyle[iii]) but at Leith the pressure was set by the operating pressure of the spheres.

Keith's first design decision was to eliminate the ammonia gas line to the Nitram plant. He wanted to use the existing pipe bridge and there wasn't room. The old gas line was barely used, and it was occupying the space he needed for his new liquid lines.

Keith made a simple calculation. The annual saving in electricity gained by sending ammonia gas to the Nitram plant, instead of turning it back into a liquid in the refrigeration plant, was £1,000 a year. The cost of a new pipe bridge was £20,000. A no-brainer. The new pipe bridge was removed from the scope of design and preparations made for the decommissioning and removal of the ammonia gas line.

Mistake number one, although it wasn't uncovered until after Keith vanished.

New pipelines meant new valves were also required.

A valve is a sort of tap. It allows you to start and stop flow.

There are many different types of valve: gate valves, needle valves, globe valves and ball valves. Valves that just go on and off, valves that you can adjust to control the flow, manual valves and remotely operated valves. Valves with washers to dissuade the liquid from coming out of the operating handle, valves with bellows seals to ensure that washers don't leak. For every type of valve there are hundreds of manufacturers.

The valves selected for the new liquid ammonia line were ball valves. Imagine a spherical ball of metal with a hole drilled through the middle like a tunnel. Then sit the ball inside a frame so the hole lines up with an inlet and outlet pipe. Whatever's in the pipe flows freely through the valve. Connect the ball to a handle, sealed by a washer in the shape of a flat doughnut. Rotate it a quarter turn and the hole is now sealed against the casing, preventing flow.

The manufacturer who had originally supplied the valves for the ammonia pipelines was W——, named after the town in which manufacture began.

Keith needed hundreds of new valves, so he followed head office guidelines and went out to tender. Competitive bidding is an excellent way to keep costs down. The only trouble is getting the specification detailed enough so that everyone is bidding for the same thing.

This was Keith's second big mistake. When he specified the new valves, he looked at normal operating conditions. The spheres were maintained at between seven times atmospheric pressure (the pressure at which the safety relief valves lifted) and two times. This was equivalent to a temperature range of plus twenty degrees centigrade to minus ten degrees centigrade.

The company with the best offer were called H——. There was an overall saving of £2,000.

Unknown to Keith, there were subtle differences between the W valves and the H valves.

W—— had quoted for exactly the same valves supplied many years ago when the first ammonia spheres were installed at Leith. In the W valves a tiny hole was drilled on one side of that ball. This meant that, when the valve was closed, any liquid trapped inside the ball would not overpressurise, but instead escape in one direction: you could choose downstream or upstream relief. The W valves had no copper or brass parts. But most importantly, the W valves had been designed to operate at minus thirty-three degrees centigrade, the lowest temperature that liquid ammonia could reach. At normal altitudes that is.

H—— had quoted for valves that were suitable for the duty exactly as specified – between minus ten and plus twenty degrees centigrade. There were no copper parts in contact with ammonia, but the handles contained brass bushes.

The new piping and valves were installed. Before allowing a hazardous material like ammonia into a new pipe, the pipe must first be integrity tested. The easy thing to use would be compressed air to bring it up to design pressure and listen for leaks. However, pneumatic testing is dangerous. There is a huge amount of stored energy in a compressed gas. If it finds a weak point, pieces of shrapnel can be ejected like rockets and fly into the soft tissue of the observers. So, for safety reasons, hydraulic testing is preferred.

John was in charge of preparing for the hydrotest. He and Brodie rigged up the hoses.

In mistake number three, Keith, the engineer, had failed to instruct the piping designer to include vents, so Bob the fitter had to loosen the bolts on the flanges that connected the pipes together. As the water flowed in, the air hissed out. Once water was flowing out from the highest point, they knew that the system was full and Bob the fitter tightened the bolts back up.

Tall Willy, the chief engineer, connected the hydraulic hand pump and slowly raised the pressure to start the test. Liquids are almost incompressible, which means that it takes very little energy to increase the pressure of a liquid. And if there is a leak, the release of a tiny drop of water is enough to bring it back to atmospheric pressure. The piping failed the test the first time. Bob the fitter soon found the culprit, a weeping thermocouple. Temperature probes are instruments, and union agreements meant that one trade was not allowed to do another's work. Bob couldn't touch the leaking instrument, even though he reckoned that it only needed two turns with a shifter. They called out Craig, the tiffy, and he replaced the thermocouple. The second time they tried, the new piping remained at the test pressure for twenty minutes.

Tall Willy signed off the test and instructed John to drain and dry the system ready for commissioning.

In mistake number four, Keith, the engineer, had failed to instruct the piping designer to include drains at the lowest points. Willy had gone home for his tea, otherwise he would have realised that the pressure test was negated when Bob the fitter split all the flanges at the low points to let the water out. Fortunately for the inhabitants of North Edinburgh, Bob was a good fitter and took special care to remake the joints securely after the water had drained away.

Draining pipes is trickier than you might think. In mistake number five, Keith, the engineer, had failed to instruct the piping designer to provide a slight incline on the long run of pipe between flanges. He had also underestimated the number of pipe supports required. What appears to be a perfectly horizontal length of rigid pipe does in fact sag between supports. It is impossible to drain the liquid at the bottom of the sag.

If you can't drain a pipe of water, you certainly can't dry it.

Drying things in Scotland has always been a challenge. It rains a lot. Wool has a natural layer of lanolin which is waterproof, as is skin, so kilts and bare legs make more sense than you might think.

John did his best. He set up a compressor to blow air through the pipes, but it passed over the water like cold wind over a lake.

In the morning Tall Willy was back with the commissioning manager, to introduce ammonia into the new piping. Padlocks were removed, final connections made.

The system was inspected one last time. The chief engineer signed off that it was mechanically complete. The commissioning manager hummed and hawed. He was annoyed that Keith, the project engineer, in mistake number six, had not provided any spare connections to allow the gradual introduction of ammonia gas to the new pipeline before connecting the pressurised liquid, but after a bit of growling, he signed off to say that it was safe to take chemicals. The services section manager signed his acceptance.

Slowly, John introduced liquid ammonia into the expanse of empty pipe.

Bang!

Thirty-three

Equilibrium

Before we investigate what happened next, a word about thermodynamic equilibrium.

Equilibrium is a beautiful thing.

For a pure liquid in equilibrium with its vapour, if you know the pressure, you automatically know the temperature and vice versa. If warm ammonia liquid were to spill on to the ground at sea level, vapour would flash off leaving the liquid at exactly minus thirty-three degrees centigrade[37].

The temperature in the spheres at Leith Fertiliser Works was kept just above zero degrees centigrade, so the pressure inside was about four atmospheres. You would experience equivalent pressure if you were to dive down thirty metres in a freshwater lake – Wastwater in Cumbria would do – or twenty-eight metres in the lightly salty North Sea, or twenty-five metres in the saline soup of the Dead Sea.

On the top of Mount Everest, with a lower atmospheric pressure, the liquid would be even colder, but I don't recommend carrying a flask of anhydrous ammonia all the way up there just to check. Better to take food, water and oxygen. Trust me on this one.

But what has any of this got to do with the unfolding emergency at Leith? Bear with me. Remember the cooling and throttling of the Joule-Thomson effect?

If you open the valve of a pressure cooker, steam roars out into the kitchen. As the pressure inside falls from twice atmospheric pressure to normal, the liquid's temperature drops from one hundred and twenty to one hundred degrees centigrade. The energy is released in great clouds of steam.

When you allow pressurised liquid ammonia to expand into an unpressurised pipe, you get a similar effect. It's Joule-Thomson throttling all over again. As the pressure drops, the liquid ammonia boils and the temperature plummets. Any water in the pipe freezes into solid ice. A huge volume of ammonia gas flashes off, providing a great rush of motive energy, propelling the newly formed ice projectiles along the pipe at high speed until they hit a bend.

Bang indeed!

Thirty-four

Vessel Entry

The new ammonia pipeline bucked and squirmed so violently that the whole pipe bridge jumped and twisted as the series of shocks shuddered away from the point where the liquid ammonia was introduced, towards the spheres.

Visibly shaken, the trio of engineers abandoned the task, closed the ammonia valves and replaced the padlocks before scuttling off to the office to discuss what had gone wrong.

They soon reached the conclusion that the new pipeline had not been properly drained after the hydrotest. As the liquid ammonia flashed down to atmospheric pressure and minus thirty-three degrees centigrade in the almost-empty pipeline, the residual water must have been simultaneously frozen into ice bullets and propelled by the flashing gas at supersonic speed.

Bullets don't take corners too well.

In conclusion, it was entirely John's fault; he should have drained the line properly.

They did not consider the impossibility of the task.

Tall Willy insisted on a thorough examination of all equipment potentially impacted by flying ice bullets. The pipe bridge was inspected: a few loose bolts had to be tightened, and the warped or cracked struts replaced.

The new pipe was checked with an ultrasonic probe, with particular attention to the bends. The wall thickness appeared unchanged. A lot of noise but no harm done. But the sphere was too thickly insulated for an external inspection; a vessel entry was required.

As punishment for his earlier misdemeanours, John was charged with getting the sphere ready and organising the physical disconnection from all live pipework.

The original storage installation was well constructed. An ICI design guide had been put together by an engineer who had operated and maintained plants at Billingham and Severnside. If a complex vessel must be inspected regularly, your design has to make it easy to do it right.

Each pipeline had a short spool – a removable section of pipe – between the last valve on the pipeline and the point where it entered the sphere. After those nearest valves were closed and locked, the sphere was pumped empty.

Production continued, using ammonia from the other two spheres, and the common pipelines remained full of ammonia under pressure. Bob, the fitter, was tasked with removing the spools between each live pipeline and the empty sphere. Fitting a blank, a thick metal disc bolted to the downstream side of the valve, would ensure no ammonia accidentally entered the sphere through a leaking valve.

The high pressure pipelines were fitted with a double block and bleed: two valves with a small test valve in-between.

Bob was working on the new pipe when a strange thing happened. The two valves at the end of a pipe full of ammonia were closed. When he opened the bleed valve in-between them, it proved that the upstream valve was holding, and it was safe to remove the spool. But when he started to disconnect the spool, ammonia began to pour out of the closed valve. Bob donned his breathing set, tightened the spool back up and moved away.

He needed a water hose to clean up the area. John was a tidy man and made sure hoses were not left lying around the site. This was annoying for the fitters and operators as they regularly needed to wash away small spills or add water to a phosphoric acid reactor when filtration was poor, so most crews had a secret stash of such things.

Alternatively, Becksy could be relied upon to find whatever was needed, bypassing the stores and the rigorous inspection process implemented by Tall Willy.

The hose stash was empty and Becksy could not be found, so Bob had to call John. Together they carried a long water hose from the store and connected it to the nearest tap.

In mistake number seven, Keith, the design engineer, had removed a water line and hose points when he redesigned the ammonia piping, so they had to run the hose up and over the pipe bridge to avoid laying it across the roadway. John inhaled deeply as Bob washed away the ammonia spill.

John asked Bob what had happened, and when Bob explained, John didn't believe him. Show me, he said.

John stood back while Bob put on his breathing apparatus. Dressed like a scuba diver in a green PVC suit with a face mask and oxygen cylinder, Bob opened the bleed valve again to show John there was no leak.

But the moment Bob loosened a bolt between the open spool and closed valve, liquid ammonia poured out. Exactly as before.

John scratched his head as he washed the spill away. Removing an empty, open piece of pipe couldn't possibly create a leak.

John called Roderick, the maintenance manager. He didn't believe it either. They showed him and then washed away the evidence.

Roderick called Tall Willy, the chief engineer. The pantomime was repeated but this time the valve handle also fell off.

The operation was halted.

Tall Willy went to see Keith, the design engineer, and together they looked at the valve specification. It was Tall Willy who spotted the mistake. The minimum design temperature was minus ten degrees centigrade – fine for normal operation. But we now know that ammonia draining to atmosphere will drop to minus thirty-three degrees centigrade. When exposed to a temperature so much lower than designed for, the ball and sealing parts inside the valve shrank. So long as the spool was connected to the valve, the valve internals were retained. As soon as the spool was released the internals began to poke though and ammonia found a path round the flash-frozen, shrinking ball.

The release of ammonia attacked the brass washer between the ball and valve handle. Ammonia and copper form a green salt which crumbles.

Over the next few years, they replaced all the H valves with W valves.

At a cost of £100,000.

The problem was diagnosed, but the valves could not be replaced immediately, and the inspection of the sphere still had to go ahead. The manholes on the spheres were removed, the inside was washed with water and blowers inserted to clear the air inside.

It had been decided not to fill the sphere with water and use Willy's boat. A full inspection had been carried out only a month before, and there was only one area that needed re-inspection – right opposite the pipe entry – where ice bullets might have damaged the vessel. A small scaffold was erected.

Even if you are not claustrophobic, it is uncomfortable to be in a confined space. The inside of the sphere was brightly lit and well ventilated, but it was still a cave. Perched at the top of a platform, the technician charged with inspection felt a long way from the manhole and daylight.

Keith was upset about the valve debacle. It wasn't his fault. After all, how was he to know about the peculiar behaviour of ammonia at atmospheric pressure? He was not a man who wasted time in multi-disciplinary meetings and point-less discussions. He had requested a written statement of the operating conditions, been provided with a document and used it to specify the valves. Why should he take the blame?

He fumed as he watched the preparation for inspection of the sphere. His carefully planned programme was ruined, his contractors on standby, twiddling their thumbs and causing mischief. There was no end in sight for the exponential overspend.

Keith was a man who prided himself on delivering projects on time and to budget. Whether the project was what the customer needed was up to them. They specified: he delivered. No more and no less. Whether it worked in practice or made economic sense was outside the scope of his service. Change was the enemy. It had to be refused, controlled or charged at a rate that discouraged it. His job was to complete exactly what he promised at the start. And move on to the next project.

Of course, Keith was concerned about safety. It had become a key metric on any project and he soon learned that the trick was to sack a few men in the first few weeks. Pick some obvious violations – failure to hold the handrails when going up stairs, missing ear defenders when using a pneumatic jack, incorrect footwear or missing safety glasses. That set the tone of the project, instilled some healthy fear, and ensured that the project team knew exactly who was boss.

So Keith was doubly upset that the valves had been logged as a project safety issue. Another example of gross unfairness. The safety issue was operational, not project related, and as he repeated for the umpteenth time in his written protest, he had used the specification he had been given.

Keith had a particular problem with John. The shift foreman refused to follow the project procedures, to issue written requests or instructions.

Instead of having permits ready for the project team to start at 7am prompt, John always wanted to walk the job, talk to the men who would carry out the work, delay the start, waste time. John was a law unto himself.

Keith knew that confined space entry was one of the most dangerous activities on site. On a statistical basis, he understood that the most dangerous chemicals were water and nitrogen, that far more people die from drowning or asphyxiation than from any other cause.

Keith walked up to the sphere. The standby man sat outside the manhole, radio in one hand and foghorn in the other, keeping an eye on the man inside. In the case of difficulty his job was not to rescue the man, but to sound the alarm.

In many confined space accidents, there are multiple fatalities. The oxygen level, normally above 20 per cent, falls to below 10 per cent and the man inside becomes first confused and lethargic and then faints. His mate goes to rescue him and is overcome in turn. The factory heroes pile in. They are all dead within a few minutes.

Keith walked around, checking the isolations, looking for something that John had done wrong. Something he could point out and complain about. Every pipeline to the sphere had been physically disconnected, and the valve on the live side closed, padlocked and blanked off.

He was about to walk away when he noticed that the drain valve at the bottom of the sphere was still closed. The pipeline beneath it was disconnected, but to maximise natural ventilation inside the sphere, surely the valve should be open?

He returned to the project Portakabin, checked the factory procedure, and wrote a report. He sat at the desk, drumming his fingers, before making a decision. His final mistake.

Keith walked back out to the spheres and gave the drain valve handle a quarter turn.

The ball inside the four-inch valve was full. There was no tiny hole drilled on one side to release the contents when it was closed. It contained half a litre of anhydrous ammonia trapped under pressure. When Keith opened the valve, the ammonia escaped. The flash gas billowed upwards into the sphere as the liquid splashed onto to the ground. Straight onto Keith's boot, where it reached its equilibrium temperature of minus thirty-three degrees centigrade.

The technician perched atop the platform inside the sphere took a single breath of the pungent vapour. His throat constricted and his eyes started to water. At five parts per million it was doing him no harm, but the smell was unbearable. He panicked. Unable to see where the ladder was, but aware of daylight through the manhole, he jumped.

The technician broke both his legs.

Keith lost a toe to frostbite.

And his job.

John noticed Keith's first mistake about one year later. It was spring and he was struggling to maintain a sufficiently low pressure in the spheres, even with the refrigeration plant running flat out. He was worried about how he would keep the pressure down when summer came. He had also noticed that there was a thick layer of ice on the outside of the spheres, which made no sense.

A young engineer was asked to look at the refrigeration. She talked to a handsome refrigeration plant salesman who took her out to lunch and convinced her that the condensers were fouled and needed a good pickling. They were duly cleaned, but the pressure went on rising. The salesman suggested an overhaul of the compressors and some new condensers. The young engineer presented the solution to company management and they agreed to go ahead with the small investment.

The pressure kept rising, and the layer of ice got thicker and thicker.

When one of the safety relief valves lifted, letting out a small puff of ammonia gas and setting off all the site alarms, the technical manager called for help from head office.

The experienced engineer who arrived the same day took in the situation with one glance. He estimated from the layer of ice on the outside of the spheres, that the ammonia liquid was very cold, well below zero degrees centigrade. For pure ammonia that meant the pressure should be four atmospheres. The actual pressure was closer to five. The only explanation was that the ammonia in the spheres was not pure. There must be something else in there.

'What has changed?' he asked.

'Nothing important,' they said.

They showed him the improvements to the refrigeration plant. He shook his head. Unnecessary, but no harm done.

'Where does the flash gas go to?' he asked.

'To the Nitram plant,' said the granulation plant manager.

The Nitram plant boss shook his head. 'Not since the upgrade; it only goes to your plant now.'

'Not in the new process it doesn't,' said the granulation plant manager. 'It hasn't for years.'

Eureka.

For a pure liquid, if you know the temperature, you automatically also know the vapour pressure of its gas. Pure substances are rarely found outside the laboratory. The ammonia from ICI Billingham also contained some inert gases. These important facts were unknown to Keith, the mechanical engineer who specified the ammonia feed to the new ammonium nitrate plant.

The high-pressure ammonia in the rail tankers contained 0.0005 per cent dissolved nitrogen. Less than 0.1 gram in a twenty-tonne rail tanker. A single grain of fine salt in a bathtub. In the lower pressure of the spheres, the nitrogen came out of solution into the vapour. The liquid, free of dissolved gas, was pumped out to make fertiliser, so the nitrogen accumulated. It had nowhere to go. With six tankers a day, five days a week, fifty-two weeks a year, the concentration of nitrogen gas had risen from 0.0005 per cent to 1 per cent.

The head office engineer sent for empty rail cars. They released the gas from the spheres into the rail cars and sent them back to Billingham.

A new pipe bridge and a new flash gas line was built, costing many times what it would have cost if it had been included in the original project. By the time summer came, the pressure in the spheres was well under control and there was no layer of ice on the outside.

Except when John was on duty and wanted to check the level.

Thirty-five

Cannoli

John is not entirely surprised to see Detective Inspector Rose Irvine at the café when he arrives for his dinner at 11.30am. He has been wondering when she will be back in touch. But he is irritated to find her on the wrong side of the table they shared last time. His table. His side. His chair. Certain routines are inviolable. If you mess up the order of things, then there is no knowing what will happen next. Entropy, the natural tendency of things to fall apart, is the enemy.

She waves at him.

'Punching above your weight, old man.' Giuseppe leers and winks.

John ignores them both and takes an empty table, stony faced.

After a few minutes, Rose appears at his side.

'Might I buy you lunch?' she asks.

John shakes his head.

'May I speak with you?'

'Any news?'

The detective inspector runs a hand through her hair. Fine, fair hair with a touch of ginger. Strawberry blonde his wife called it. The hair reminds him of Polly. Only the hair. Any resemblance stops there. The policewoman has bright eyes and clear skin. A woman who enjoys her food but exercises as well. Plump and soft in the right places. Lean and strong where it matters.

'Yes,' she says.

Back in control again, John rises and pulls out the opposite chair. His face relaxes into a more genial expression as they both order the specials – *arancini* and *pollo Milanese*.

He waits until Giuseppe brings their drinks – Irn-Bru for her and house wine for him – before asking. 'What's the crack?'

'We found Fraser.' She pushes a letter across the table to him. 'Alive and well and working in a bank.'

Exactly the sort of job that would suit the lad. Numbers. Safe, warm and boring. Some of the men called Fraser an auld wifey. John would never use that as an insult; he maintains the highest respect for old women.

John scans the letterhead, recognising the logo from the Clydesdale Bank. He does not bother to read the letter, so her next words take him by surprise.

'What does Fraser mean about the business with Polly?'

He looks up at her.

Why is he surprised? She is whip-smart. It was just a matter of time before she found out. They must have records, after all.

John sighs and casts his mind back to the coldest day of the century, the day it happened.

At the time, John didn't know it was the coldest day of the century, he only found out later, on the news. He was too busy struggling through icy winds and flurries of snow to produce fertiliser that nobody wanted.

The price of imported fertiliser had plummeted. Thanks to the planned economy and unreasonable optimism of the Soviet Union, supply in the east vastly exceeded demand, and NPK fertiliser was being exchanged for desperately sought-after hard currency at less than the cost of manufacture.

On the edge of Leith docks, the wind whipped the seawater into huge waves. They crashed onto the road as the estuary attempted to claim back the land.

The waste heat from the factory was usually enough to keep the snow from settling. The heat of reaction, dissipated through steam leaks and missing lagging, normally kept the factory roads clear.

Not tonight. Snowdrifts, up to waist height, lay in wait for the unwary. Water channels burrowed through the drifts, snaking their way to the drains inside a thin tunnel of ice, deceptively covered in snow.

The yellow sodium lighting and white snow made the factory eerily beautiful. Dagger-sharp stalactites hung from external walkways. The three shining, silver ammonia storage spheres sported skirts of ice and a light dusting of snow on the windward side. The tall nitric acid absorption column swayed slightly in the wind, making the helical ribbon of lights that snaked around it seem to wink like Christmas lights.

It was already dark when John passed through the entry gates to the docks at Bernard Street. He glanced up at the old Grain Trading Market, now a scaffolding store, with the original carved stone frieze still visible above the doors. Plump cherubs, tiny oxen and huge ploughs depicted the farming calendar of ploughing, sowing and reaping. Improbably shaped ships transported the harvest to foreign lands.

The wrought iron dock gates were chained open and the road led past a container warehouse and over the turntable bridge to the SAI factory. In the freezing cold, the cheery lights from the gatehouse guided him to the turnstile gate.

Through the window, he could see a computer terminal connected to the weighbridge, two television screens that picked up each of the storage areas in turn, a sink, a kettle and a valiant electric heater running a losing battle against the draughts. The walls were bare brick and the woodwork was stained yellow with nicotine.

Beyond the gatehouse, the office block sat in darkness. Locked up for the weekend to keep the canteen from pilferers, the telex from misuse, the clean floor from dirty boots.

Opposite the gatehouse was a Portakabin that housed John's office as shift manager. He entered via a narrow cloakroom, hanging his snow-damp anorak on a peg before retrieving his mug from a padlocked steel locker. A second door opened into a brightly lit office with two desks. Each desk had a phone and a logbook, but no computer. Personal computers were still prohibitively expensive back in the early 1980s, and written communication was by letter or, if urgent, telex.

The desk and walls were wood-effect Formica with double-glazed windows on two sides, one looking back towards the gatehouse, the main route in and out of the site, and the other pointing up the road to the factory beyond.

'Filthy night.'

'Aye.'

John walked past his oppo, the retiring shift manager, to a small kitchenette at the back of the office which held a fridge, kettle, electric stove and oven.

The kettle was already hot, but the other shift managers knew better than to fill the teapot. John's requirements were very precise when it came to his first cup of tea. His colleagues had borne the brunt of his weaponised laughter too many times over the years and learned to let him make it himself.

The business with Polly.
It was a shift he would never forget.
It started badly.
And got worse.

John was at the gatehouse, along with Alec and Blind Willy, waiting for the shift kiss, when Daisy knocked on the gatehouse window. She was dressed for work: high heels, short skirt and low top, shivering inside a thin coat. 'Youse seen Polly?' she mouthed.

John shook his head and opened the sliding hatch.

'The bairn's with her gran.' Daisy wiped away a tear. 'It's not like her to leave wee Laura fer sae long. I'm worried.'

John let Daisy through the turnstile and into the gatehouse. He gave her a hanky and a boiled sweet and asked questions before offering to phone the police.

Alec looked away, shaking his head. As an ex-policeman Alec knew exactly how the Leith Police would respond to a prozzy reporting a missing colleague: dismissively.

Blind Willy asked Daisy to sit on his lap. Just as well he didn't see the look of disgust that crossed her face at the scar tissue on his. She left after extracting a promise from John to keep his eyes and ears open.

Minutes after Daisy left, an alarm went off in the gatehouse to announce the arrival of a telex. John lost no time in crossing the road to the empty office block, unlocking the main door and communications room to pick up the ticker tape. A red alert. He cursed. Just as he feared.

The Leith factory was on an interruptible power supply. Rather than build more power plants to cope with transient peaks, the Scottish Central Electricity Generating Board gave a lower tariff to those factories willing to reduce power consumption at times of high electricity demand.

Any minute now, the whole of Scotland would simultaneously plug in their kettles, turn on their ovens and sit down to watch TV in front of an electric fire.

Within thirty minutes of the red alert message, factory power had to be reduced to 10 per cent of normal consumption: all but essential equipment stopped. Failure to do so would lead to an increase in the electricity bill to the tune of hundreds of thousands of pounds.

John called Blind Willy at the gatehouse, who opened the book with the laminated emergency procedures. Running his left pinkie across the Braille, he read the load shedding message over the Tannoy. Alec sounded the siren. The rest of the team sprang into action.

The shutdown sequence was well rehearsed.

With the press of a single button, the process of melting sulphur stopped immediately. The sudden cessation of power to the electrical elements allowed the cooling molten sulphur to assume fabulous shapes. Yellow sculptures formed: scorpions with crystalline shells and giant pincers; twisting, swirling worms and snakes; smooth spherical blobs of giant spider bodies with drip-down stalactites for legs. John shuddered at the yellow monsters emerging though sulphurous mist.

As the molten sulphur solidified, the production of sulphur dioxide, then sulphur trioxide stopped. The dilution plant ran on for twenty minutes, reducing the concentration of oleum – that super-concentrated sulphuric acid – to prevent it freezing in tanks and pipes, exporting 70 per cent sulphuric acid until the product tanks were full.

The flow of sulphuric acid to the phosphoric acid reactor

ran on until the phosphate rock conveyors had all been manually stopped. The recycle and export phosphoric acid pumps continued until the tipping Prayon filter slowed to a halt with one of the pans poised to release the gypsum.

All across the factory, lights flashed, alarms shrieked and howled: the control system unable to distinguish between deliberate actions and inadvertent failure.

The antiquated superphosphate plant had to be shut down manually. It used little power, but was a batch plant, easy to sacrifice.

Ammonia refrigeration was switched over to diesel power. The backup power generators could provide only a fraction of the power the factory needed, sized for safety-critical and emergency operation only. The diesel generators woke from cold slumber with angry protests, clattering and shaking as they gathered speed, belching out clouds of black smoke before settling down to a low thrum.

The feeds to the granulator and ammonium nitrate prilling tower were interrupted and a slow runout began. Only then could the huge seawater pumps powering the vacuum ejectors and gas scrubbers be stopped.

Only the nitric acid plant was left running, turned down to the very minimum production rate, the excess steam whistling out into the cold, clear air. It generated more than enough steam to sustain itself and feed the rest of the site. But if it stopped, there was not enough steam on site to start it back up, so it operated continuously for two years between planned maintenance shutdowns. A package boiler was hired in for the start-up, at ruinous expense.

John watched the needle on the power meter in the motor control centre. He knew the power rating of every single piece of equipment on the site and could solve multi-order simultaneous equations in his head without realising what he was doing. He saw in his mind's eye the effect of each of the motors shutting down. When he spotted an unusual trend, he knew who was late and bellowed down the phone at the plant operator. In twenty-three minutes, they were below the electricity consumption target, and it was with pride that he walked over to the office to send the confirmation telex to the SCEGB.

Twenty-three minutes, a new record.

John did his rounds, sharing the record result, congratulating the men who had worked fastest, berating those slower off the mark, handing out work for them to do while the factory was shut down. He found them control room floors to mop, cabinet tops to dust, lightbulbs to change, storerooms to tidy, permits to file, training updates to read. No idle hands on his shift.

Without the normal noises of conveyors rattling and motors turning, the sound of John's footsteps crunching though snow gave each shift-team member plenty of warning of his approach. That and the bush telegraph, a relay of phone calls as he left one control room and headed for the next. Enough time to wake up and look busy.

A strange melancholy gripped John and he headed back to his office. Away from the only section still working – alive with the purr of nitric acid pumps, the whistle of waste steam, the thrum of diesel generators – an eerie silence descended on the rest of the factory. Without the familiar noises of production, with all but emergency lighting turned off, the towers and columns, tanks and spheres, gantries and whalebone sheds took on a sinister form. Familiarity without warmth. Like viewing a corpse.

John shivered, the hairs on the back of his neck stiffened, a moment of premonition. He crunched across the packing yard and cursed as the thin ice beneath the snow cracked, and freezing water trickled into his boots.

A few hours later the telex alarm sounded again. The Scottish Central Electricity Generating Board gave the factory permission to power back up. John phoned the works manager to suggest that they wait until after Scotland's breakfast. He reasoned that it was not the first time that they had restarted only to be shut down again. He didn't mention that he had no appetite for spending the rest of his shift wrestling with the seawater pumps only to be told off for not having done it faster by people who had no conception of the added difficulty of darkness, foul weather and fatigue.

The works manager told John to man up and get on with it.

Nothing much worked in the factory without seawater. It provided cooling to control reactions and the motive force for the ejectors that sucked the vacuum. It slurried the gypsum before it was pumped out to sea and it cleaned the gases so they could be safely sent up the chimneys – although it barely touched the mercaptans released by Jordanian phosphate.

Stopping the seawater pumps was easy, but bringing them back to life was an art.

John chose Fraser to assist him. The boy needed some toughening up. For an easy life, John could have selected Brodie, but John was a man who developed his team without the need for competency spreadsheets and training databases. Scrupulously fair, he shared the dirtiest jobs out. The fact that it would cause disproportionate pain to a man like

Fraser, while it would be seawater off a duck's back to Brodie, didn't enter his reasoning.

The first task was to check the screens. The screens were huge rectangular filters made of several layers of coarse mesh in iron frames, set in the seawall to cover the seawater inlets to the factory. The huge seawater pumps had such powerful suction that they would otherwise pull in all sorts of flotsam and jetsam.

The screens could be lowered and raised by cast iron winches on the dock. Even with the assistance of gears and pulleys, it was hard work to pull each one up. John took one winch and directed Fraser to another. The boy was young and strong, but John still had his screen out of the water first. As the cast iron chain squealed against the pulleys, a man emerged from the shadows. John was perturbed to see Becksy. A good shift manager always knew who was on site. He made a mental note to remonstrate with Tall Willy. If a day shift man worked overtime, the shift team needed to be informed. However, he was glad of the assistance. Older and slighter than either of them, Becksy still made short shrift of the task, and the middle screen was level with the dockside long before Fraser and John had hauled the other screens to rest beside it.

The worst job was cleaning the screens.

Fraser was not keen on the eels trapped in the mesh and left it to Becksy to yank them out, discarding the dead ones, collecting the live ones, wriggling and slithering, in an empty bucket. Becksy could always be relied upon to find a use, or a stomach, for anything and everything on site.

Fraser lowered another bucket on a rope in order to collect seawater to wash away the fine strawberry blonde threads that were caught in the screen. There were many more eels below. It looked like a feeding frenzy down there. When the bucket hit the water the writhing, wriggling, snake-fish dispersed, and he saw what had attracted them there in the first place.

There wasn't much left of Polly. What remained in the water was bloated beyond recognition. Only the tufts of strawberry blonde hair still clinging to her scalp identified her.

Becksy howled and fell to his knees. He crossed himself and bowed his head, his lips moving in silent prayer.

Fraser turned away from the sea and vomited on the dock-side, bringing up the remains of a surprisingly respectable meat pie and diced carrots.

John called the police.

Becksy kept a silent vigil beside Polly's floating body, hanging from a cast iron ladder with one arm while the other prevented her from floating away. The smell of iodine and diesel in the water masked the stench of putrefaction. As the recovery boat approached, the lap and splash of water against the wharf grew louder, the cast iron chains rattled against concrete, but Becksy remained focused on his task. He paid no heed to the howling siren that split the night. It was only the reflection of the flashing blue light on black water that caused Becksy to look up. He raced up the rusty ladder and ran towards John. Eyes and mouth wide open, beads of sweat glistening in the moonlight as they ran down his temples. Fear. More than fear, abject terror. Becksy was afraid of the police. Why?

For a moment, John wondered if Becksy knew something about Polly's death. He dismissed the thought in an instant. The distress he exhibited at the discovery, the tenderness with which he defended her body from eels, none of this spoke of a guilty conscience. Becksy was not a sophisticated man, and his actions didn't lie.

If the police were going to look for a murderer, they would start with the punters. Or her pimp. Or her dealer who was probably also her pimp. And perhaps no third party was needed. Pacing the docks on high heels in treacherous, icy conditions, in the dark, off your face. A slip was all it would take.

Poor Polly.

Becksy raised a finger to his lips, narrowing his eyes, wrinkling his brow, imploring John to let him leave. John nodded and Becksy melted into the shadows.

After the police divers and ambulance left, John remained at the dockside, shoulders hunched, head bowed, gazing down into the unforgiving sea. He stood silent and motionless for a long time and then he said some kind words to Polly. He hoped she was at peace. He hoped that she had drowned long before her hair caught in the pump suction.

The night shift crew finished the job of cleaning the seawater screens. The factory was running again by the time dawn broke.

Just after shift changeover, the SCEGB sent a telex red alert to shut the factory down again. John took no pleasure in being right, he was too sad about Polly. He closed his eyes and imagined all her cares sinking to the bottom of Victoria dock as her pretty soul soared upwards to paradise.

A flurry of hailstones rattles at the windows of the Italian café in Canonmills. Outside, the sky has darkened; lunch service has finished and Rose and John are alone in the café, apart from Giuseppe, who offers them dessert.

The cannoli are little pastry cylinders stuffed with cream.

John encourages Rose to order. She tries to refuse, but her resistance crumbles easily. Just like the pastry.

John likes that she takes such pleasure in food, wonders if she has a man at home who cooks for her after a long day policing. Guesses not. He can usually tell. The story of Polly's demise has clearly upset her, and yet she must come across terrible things every day. He is glad that she hasn't lost her compassion. He guesses that she needs time by herself and suggests that they call it a day after coffee.

She agrees. 'Come to the station first thing tomorrow.'

John shakes his head. 'I cannae.'

He clocks the concern on her face and relents.

'Doctor's appointment the morn's morn.'

'Afterwards?'

'Aye.'

Ninth Clue

WHISKY BOTTLE

GRANULATION

Thirty-six

Empty Whisky Bottle with Hairy String

The hospital appointment is a routine check. Since John's operation, shortly after retirement, the surgeon likes to keep an eye on him. A physician's pride is at stake, and John doesn't mind being a guinea pig for the medical students. He likes to watch their wee faces when they listen to him breathing, see the confusion that twists their lips and furrows their brows, the cold sweat at the temples as it dawns on them that they've discovered something awful, the fear that they are going to have to break bad news to him.

Streptomycin[38] arrived at the end of the Second World War, just in time for John. A few months later and the TB would have taken the other lung as well. As it is, he can get by pretty well on half capacity, and who needs a full set of ribs anyway?

The consultant chides him for bringing a bottle of whisky, reminds him that NHS staff can't accept gifts and pretends that he'll enter it into a charity raffle, before giving the standard spiel on the dangers of alcohol that both know will be ignored.

John takes a bus to Torphichen Street, where Detective Inspector Rose Irvine is waiting for him in the police interview room.

Unlike the gift John just gave the doctor, the bottle of

Glenlivet single malt in the evidence tray is empty. The bottle has a string round its neck. About six feet of the stuff. Hairy string, brown and fuzzy, the kind that burns your hands if you let it slide through too fast, little fibres snatching at the flesh and worming their way under the skin.

John picks it up and tells her what he knows.

The whisky came from the bonded warehouse on Sally Street. Big Stu had an understanding with the night watchman. Every time there was a major movement – a lorry arriving from the distillery, a shipping container to be loaded for Brazil, six hundred bottles to be stacked and secured – a box of six would crash to the concrete floor and shatter, a breakage rate of 1 per cent, only to be expected.

Over time, the owners of the warehouse noticed that the breakage rate was not just about 1 per cent, but an unvarying exact 1.000%. When you drop a box of six you might expect the severity of bottle damage to vary. Sometimes one or two might break, occasionally three or four or five. But always six? The accountant became suspicious, insisting that any broken bottles be produced in evidence, which led to a roaring trade in recycled empties.

Although Big Stu made a small profit on the sale of stolen whisky, he viewed it as a calling, more noble than mere theft. He had been much impressed by the 1949 Ealing Studios comedy *Whisky Galore!* and became the Robin Hood of the bonded warehouse, the Scarlet Pimpernel of Glenlivet, a rebel with a cause who provided a service to his fellow man. Why should South Americans glug fine single malts when there were hard-working Scotsmen who had never tasted their own country's finest produce?

Big Stu had a list. Every time he got the call from the night watchman that a delivery was imminent, Big Stu selected six names from the list and collected their money and empty bottles. A few days later he delivered the whisky.

The delivery route was made complicated by John's insistence on checking the breath and bags of those entering the factory. Being caught with alcohol on site was a sackable offence. This rule did not extend to the executive dining room where sherry, wine and brandy were served at lunch on special occasions. Nor did it cover the good managers who always turned up on Hogmanay to offer the shift workers a dram to see in the New Year.

One law for the bosses, another for the workers. Various ingenious routes were devised to exchange contraband alcohol for money, but the simplest was the granulator conveyor.

A long rubber belt connected the granulation plant to the packing unit at Salamander Street. The belt returned empty, apart from the occasional bottle of malt whisky.

Big Stu would telephone the gatehouse before he sent something over.

Blind Willy would put out the Tannoy call. In the daytime it had to be something anodyne so the managers in the office wouldn't notice it, but specific enough so that the recipient understood the urgency.

'Granulation tractor driver to the stores, driver to the stores.'

At night, without bosses around to hear, the Tannoy call could be more playful.

'SS Cabinet Minister setting sail for Todday.'

'Captain Wagget requests assistance with cargo.'

The tractor driver would wait at the other end of the conveyor, catch the delivery, attach a long piece of hairy string to the bottle, and bury it beneath the mountain of fertiliser granules in the reject shed with the end of the string close to the surface, for easy retrieval.

An important part of the shift handover between tractor drivers was to identify the position of these precious bottles. They couldn't risk breaking the glass with the steel shovel of a bulldozer. The whisky never remained in place for more than a few shifts and the recipient paid the tractor driver a small fee to recover his booty.

The drivers knew to avoid the other sorts of fertiliser amid the granules. Human fertiliser. This had never been a problem until the first female engineer came along.

Outside the factory, they called her the flying hoor. There were many women in Leith docks at night, but she was the only one who drove a motorbike.

Inside the factory, they just called her trouble.

The full-time union official had been horrified when it was announced that a female engineer would be moving to Leith to work shifts. He protested to the production manager, the personnel manager, the deputy works manager. They all shook their heads and agreed with him, but instructions had come from head office and were to be obeyed. Despite a lifetime of locking horns and fighting each other, for the first time the full-time official missed the former works manager. Such a thing would never have been allowed to happen on his watch.

The deputy works manager had tried his best. He pointed to the presence of a convicted sex offender on one of the teams. Head office reminded him that the man's misdemeanours had been with men not women. They further reminded him that when they had sought assurance with regard to safeguarding young apprentices, the deputy works manager himself had explained that the man was convicted for being openly homosexual before the law changed and had lived quietly with the same lover for twenty years, a danger to no one.

He raised the practical difficulties. The showers in the amenity block were open stalls. The only female toilets were in the office block which was locked closed at night. He declared this *coup de grâce* triumphantly to head office. The reply was curt: convert one of the female toilets into a shower and give her a key to the office block.

Of course, the real problem was not her ablutions, but theirs. The main site was half a mile long, and the male toilets were in the amenity block beside the shift manager's Portakabin and at the gatehouse. No one bothered to walk down all that way. They urinated into the vacuum pump hot wells, or onto the unlagged steam pipes to hear the hiss. They dug holes in the piles of granules before adding to their fertilising properties. This was acceptable behaviour for an all-male team, but when they thought of a young girl witnessing such boorish behaviour, they felt ashamed. Shame turned to anger.

Word went around that there would be no Christmas box that year, the annual cash bonus, because of the unbudgeted cost of plumbing.

The production manager looked grim when he called John into his office and asked how best to deal with the lass until head office saw sense. John saw his opportunity. He looked serious. He shook his head at the lunacy of the pen-pushers in Ravelston. He sympathised with the difficulty that the production manager found himself in. If only it wasn't for the tension in the team, he said, he would have been happy to take her on his shift and keep an eye on her.

The production manager thought about it for a while. He knew all about the cause of the tension between John and Hughie. Hughie had been one of the union shop stewards who had humiliated John over the question of discretionary showers for contractors. John had lost the battle of the potash drivers' ablutions, but what really rankled was the failure of the Edinburgh shop stewards to support their colleagues over the closure of Stinky Miller's in Aberdeen.

What, the deputy manager asked, if he were to take Hughie off John's team and swap him with George? John thought about it and then signalled that it might just work if he gave him Norman instead. The production manager shook his head. If he moved the best man from a team that was already weak, it would just cause trouble elsewhere. They bandied names to and fro, but there was no ideal straight swap for a phosphoric acid operator.

John had never played chess, but had he been given an early chance he would have excelled at it. He knew the strengths and weaknesses of every individual in the factory. With a little ingenuity, he could reform a winning position.

By promoting one of his smarter granulation operators to phosphoric acid, he could transfer Hughie to granulation and swap him out from there.

He explained his plan and asked for Iain in return.

The production manager thought about it.

You do the training first, he asked?

John agreed.

They shook hands.

Thirty-seven

NPK Granulation

You can granulate anything, even sand and water, given the right conditions of temperature, moisture, speed of rotation and residence time.

The process for turning fine particles into larger granules with the right mix of nitrogen, phosphorus and potassium was developed by SAI with French company Grande Paroisse[G]. Elegant and simple on paper, it took skill to operate.

Solid flow was the cause of most problems. The chutes choked all the time. If the material was damp, it clung to the rubber lining and narrowed the throat. If a lump fell from the sparger through the grizzly it blocked the chute, and the rest of the material built up on top.

The chutes were kept clear with a set of valiant boxers – the politest name for them. These sturdy shafts, with hemispherical tips, plunged into soft rubber diaphragms set into the chutes. The frequency of stroke could be adjusted, along with the speed of attack, the depth of thrust, and rate of withdrawal, creating a regular, rhythmic motion.

The original action, a caressing elliptical motion set up by the French commissioning team, was the most erotic. The rather more pragmatic Scots engineers removed the testicle-shaped gearing and mechanical drive to make the willies pneumatic – just short sharp jabs back and forth. But they couldn't hide the gasps and hisses of compressed air, and the new bellows couldn't completely hide the mesmerising motion.

It was not just solids that caused distractions, the liquid flows to the granulator also carried hidden peril.

Thirty-eight

Tuatara

Granulation looks easy: you add liquid and powder to one end of a drum. Make a porridge. Heat it up and spin it round. The acids and alkalis react and release heat. Lots of it. The water evaporates, plumes of fluffy white steam soaring from the top of a high chimney. Tilt the drum, and at the other end of the rotating cylinder, hot granules emerge to be screened and cooled. The oversized stuff is smashed and added to the dust, which is recycled back to the beginning, while the correctly sized granules are conveyed into the huge whalebone sheds.

But the truth is that granulation is an art. The alkalis – liquid and gaseous ammonia, solid potash – must be balanced by the acids – phosphoric and nitric. The acid has to be just weak enough to provide water to wet the solids and bind them together as they react, but not so watery that they turn into gloopy porridge at the end.

In the art of granulation, which was nothing like the art of Dan Flavin, John was a master, a witch doctor. The Granny plant ran like clockwork on his shift. If he inherited a problem at the start of the shift – liquid emerging from the back end of the massive rotating cylinder, or the thump of giant boulders rattling and banging inside the drum – he would have fixed it by the time his shift left.

John kept secrets. Knowledge was power, and John revelled in his pre-eminence, but the main reason for his silence was that much of his problem-solving involved actions which were, if not forbidden, at least frowned upon. And even where his conduct was logical and sensible, he lacked the vocabulary or science to fully explain what he did and how he knew what to do.

Some of his directions seemed counter-intuitive. He would occasionally add more acid when the product was sloppy, increasing the liquid load further. Or when snowballs thumped around inside, he would add more solids. If he thought about it at all, he considered the granulator to be a giant gut. When you have diarrhoea, you need to drink more liquid; when you are constipated you ingest more fibre. It often worked. If the alkali ratio was too high, extra acid brought it back into balance, and the heat of reaction drove the water away. If boulders were forming instead of granules, adding more solids increased the number of potential nuclei available, and smaller granules developed. John had the benefit of experience, the courage of his convictions and the patience to wait while things got worse before they got better.

John was a self-tuning control loop. His finest quality was his patience. What appeared to be an instinctive understanding was actually born of long experience, trial and error. If he made a change, he would not try anything else until success or failure was proven, a negative result being just as important as a positive one. He read the shift logs from his days off, cast an eye over the charts and log sheets. His eagle eyes and intimate knowledge of the authors allowed him to differentiate between fabrication and honesty, between numbers written down to satisfy management and what had really been done. He would file the trends away, synapses snapping as his brain constructed a huge internal model of the process. John was an analogue supercomputer in the days of binary control. A multi-dimensional digital array at a time of linear 3-15 psi pneumatics.

You might think it easy. If you know the volume (in metres cubed) and you know the feed-rate (in metres cubed per hour) then you can calculate the residence time by dividing the former by the latter. The granulator was huge – four men, standing on each other's shoulders, in diameter; forty men, lying head to toe, in length. So, if you feed an eighty-metre long, six-metre diameter granulator with two hundred cubic metres an hour, you might expect a residence time of about half a day, twelve hours. Although it is never more than a third full – the material tumbling from the walls as it rotates, an empty core of hot gas for the fertiliser to fall through – there is also no pure plug flow, no first in/first out fairness, but a considerable amount of back-mixing, the early particles going back and interacting with newer arrivals. So in normal circumstances the results of a change at the beginning of one shift are not known until near the end. The mistake that most people make is impatience. They make a change, see no improvement, make another. The change is too big, a new problem emerges, another change is made before the effects of the last one can be felt, and so on in a vicious cycle of instability.

If there is insufficient reaction, the acids remain liquid. Without evaporation of water, the residence time changes, a slurry runs directly from one end to the other, failing to fill the rotating drum, failing to describe the complex helical path designed to pick and mix. As John liked to put it, diarrhoea – it could have passed through the eye of a camel.

If there is too much reaction, then everything builds up inside. Instead of 30 per cent full the granulator becomes dangerously overloaded, building up until the whole thing sets solid. Constipation.

John had a lizard's patience, the attention span of a tuatara. Waiting, immobile, inflexible. Happy to dig and shovel with the rest of the team if push came to shove, but always trying to find a way to avoid waste.

John also had a magic wand. A long-handled shovel that he kept hidden behind the long chute to the Granny screens. He used it to clear the sieves. The fine screen, designed to separate and recycle particles that were too small, often blinded, resulting in insufficient seed being sent back to the start of the process, and causing huge snowballs to form where Maltesers were required.

He also used it when the product was too dusty. By shovelling the fine dust off the screens onto choking piles on the floor, he ensured that less seed returned to the granulator and the granule size increased.

John's understanding of both feedback and the more complex feed-forward control was highly developed. He had never seen a Nyquist diagram, never programmed a proportional, derivative and integral control algorithm, but he knew how to watch and wait and wasn't afraid of a bit of mess in the middle.

The fertiliser factory was built next to the sea for a reason. The waste had to go somewhere. Strictly speaking Leith was not on the sea. It lay on reclaimed land in the Forth Estuary, but the water smelled of seaweed and tasted salty and that meant sea to John.

Most of the liquid waste came from the scrubbers – the towers used to remove the gases by bubbling them through recirculating liquid to trap hydrogen fluoride, oxides of sulphur and phosphorus (although not mercaptans from Jordanian phosphate rock).

The acidic scrubber liquor was neutralised with caustic soda, sodium hydroxide, to form salts like sodium sulphate, sodium fluoride and sodium phosphate, before being pumped out to sea along with the solid gypsum. The design approach was simple; there's an awful lot of salt in the sea already, a few more tonnes isn't going to make a blind bit of difference to anyone. In calm weather, the solid gypsum built up in shallow water to form a new landmass, a few hundred metres from the shore. It disappeared in rough seas, only to form again somewhere else. The seals loved to bask on this shape-shifting Gypsum Island and frolic in the slightly warmer water at the exit of the waste pipe. It is true that the gypsum – calcium sulphate from the phosphoric acid plant – also contained cadmium and small amounts of radioactive caesium from the phosphate rock. From John's point of view, it came from the ground in the first place and he was just putting it back. Unfortunately, the Scottish Environment Agency didn't see it that way, and over time they began tightening up.

In a way, that was what caused the accident. That and Fiona's inexperience.

Thirty-nine

Recycle

John had always known that women were the stronger sex – look at what they put up with to propagate the human race. He had come across a handful of female engineers in his time. All terrifying. Fishy Olga from the Russian factory boat, hard as the iron spikes she hammered into the ice of the Bering Strait to free a trapped a Royal Navy Frigate. Massachusetts Meg who fixed instruments on the aircraft carrier. And Fiona, the cause of so much new plumbing.

Not to put too fine a point on it, Fiona was not in the same league as Olga and Meg, just a pain in the neck. Confident without skill, impetuous without experience. Nothing but trouble.

The new granulation plant at SAI had pipe reactors; the sort of equipment chemical engineers get excited about. Normal reactors are just scaled-up test tubes. You add the ingredients, liquids from a pipette, solids with a spatula, one then another, they react and then you tip the product out. Or scrape it out. Or break the test tube to get it out. It's called batch production because you produce one batch at a time, then start all over again. That's a chemist's idea of process plant design.

In pipe reactors, you get the sort of plant design a practical engineer prefers. You add reactants at one end and the product comes out the other end, pushed out by more stuff being fed in all the time. It's continuous production. When everything is balanced, it can be much more efficient, but more temperamental to start up. Harder to get right, and there's another tricky aspect. Ammonium nitrate is also used as an explosive.

Pure ammonium nitrate is pretty stable unless you detonate it or set it on fire. In Oppau, Germany in 1921, attempts to unblock an ammonium nitrate silo using dynamite led to a much larger explosion and the deaths of more than 560 people. Twenty-six years later, in Texas City on Galveston Bay in 1947, a crowd gathered on the dockside to watch a spectacular fire aboard SS *Grandcamp*. Unfortunately, the ship was loaded with ammonium nitrate for French farmers, along with ammunition and bales of sisal twine. The cargo exploded and killed the crew, all but one of the town's fire brigade, and many of the spectators who came to watch the fire. Over 580 people died.

More recently, in 2013 in West Texas, USA a fire at a warehouse caused about 240 tonnes of ammonium nitrate to explode, killing fifteen people. In 2020, 2,750 tonnes of ammonium nitrate exploded in the port of Beirut, Lebanon, killing at least 220 people, injuring more than 5,000 and leaving 300,000 homeless.

So if you are going to avoid turning a pipe reactor into a pipe bomb, you need a way to remove heat. And the most efficient way to remove heat is with water. The clever French designers added a quench. If the temperature or pressure rose faster than expected, if there was so much as a hint that the reaction was running away, a deluge of water put a stop to all that. The watery mess was diverted to a slop tank. The slops could go one of two ways: back into the granulator or out to Gypsum Island.

Now, although the sea is full of sodium fluoride and calcium sulphate, it is not that full of ammonium nitrate. It's just another salt, but not one found so commonly in the sea. You might expect some fertiliser run-off from Brodie's farm, the fields stretch right down to the beautiful beach near Tantallon castle, but Brodie is a careful farmer and always waits for dry weather before spreading.

Fiona was on night shift when the pipe reactor hiccupped, and the quench went off. Everything happened as designed, and the team got ready to try again. Unfortunately, the slop tank was full. Previous quenches from previous hiccups on previous shifts had been allowed to accumulate. The high-level interlock system prevented restart until the liquid in the slop tank was removed.

Fiona had a choice. Two options.

Sending the quench into the Firth of Forth is what every other shift would do. Except they hadn't, and now the tank was full.

The lead operator's instruction was clear. Out to sea. What were the chances of an Environment Agency inspector taking any notice at one o'clock in the morning?

Fiona, being young and foolish, disagreed. She had been put on the planet to save it, her reasons for studying chemical engineering were partly altruistic. Here was the first chance to do something useful. She spoke persuasively in favour of recycling. The lead hand disagreed vehemently. He knew it was wrong, though he couldn't explain exactly why. Wrong because it was different. He made the mistake of adding some rude words about the competence of women in general and Fiona in particular.

Fiona ordered him to recycle it back to the granulator as punishment. Unfortunately, it being one o'clock in the morning, she failed to do any of the calculations she had spent four years at university being trained to do. Nor did she refresh her memory on the design criteria, which could have formed the basis for detailed instructions. All commissioning documents were locked up in the office block half a mile away and Fiona was in a hurry. She had to be at a training course at 9am the following day. In order to get a few hours' sleep, she needed to leave the site by 2am. She knew that as soon as she left, the contents would be dumped to sea, so she waited until her instructions were obeyed.

What should have been dribbled in to the pre-granulator over days was sent in one, bad-tempered, fell swoop.

The pre-granulator was a cylinder that rotated. Shorter than the main granulator and only a man and a half in diameter, it rotated to mix the discharge from the pipe reactors. Fixed wheels with thick rubber tyres pressed against steel belts that wrapped the girth of the cylinder. As the liquid from the slops tank gushed in, the solids that rose and fell in a helical dance along the length of the pre-granulator became soft and squishy, and then joined together into lumps before puddling into pancakes and then finally melting into a single liquid wave that rose and splashed back.

The lead operator watched the temperature dropping and the pre-granulator filling and the motor current rising with growing satisfaction before calling John. John ordered him to increase the feeds to get more heat in, but to no avail. By the time John had arrived in the control room, the motor current had increased until it could drive the cylinder no longer. The pre-granulator stopped. The liquid inside solidified. There was only one thing for it.

Dig it out.

Digging out a granulator, large or small, is a horrible task. Working in any confined space is uncomfortable, mentally and physically. Now add a waterproof suit with hood, thick rubber boots, goggles and a dust mask. The work was back-breaking: spades and chisels, pneumatic hammers. Tonnes and tonnes of solids to be chipped out and removed.

But despite this, digging out the granulator held a certain appeal for some men. The task was clearly defined. A vessel full of stuff that had to be shifted. There was a start and an end. There was some variation – the stuff could be light and friable, soft and sloppy, or set solid. Time was of the essence. As the granulator cooled, multiple chemical reactions continued until the solids set into a single concrete lump. This was one of the few dirty jobs that couldn't be left for the next shift; the challenge was to get as much done as possible, as fast as possible. Competitive digging. A bit like going to war, there was an enemy to be fought and it could only be conquered by superior force. It took some skill but above all, plain physical old-fashioned hard work.

First, the pre-granulator had to be made safe for entry.

The lead hand set the extract fan to maximum. He prepared the isolations: pulling the tails from the motor, padlocking the feed valves closed. He ordered the shift fitter to remove the feed spools, blank the open ends, open the doors and put more fans and extractors to work. When the air temperature was bearable and the oxygen readings showed the air to be breathable, he sent the first man inside.

Fortunately, Kelly weighed no more than eight stone, even with breathing apparatus, and he was able to walk the length of the cylinder, checking the air quality before signalling for the rest of the crew to enter.

Unfortunately, because no one had ever made the mistake of recycling the quench before, no one knew what to expect. What appeared to be a solid floor was in fact a thin crust of fertiliser, under which lay a lake of hot, caustic liquid.

Hughie was a big man. No sooner had he thrust his spade into the solid, than the thin crust he was standing on cracked and split, and his feet descended into the molten lava underneath. It was just deep enough to rise up over the top of his rubber boots, filling them with boiling liquid.

The air quality alarms went off as Hughie screamed. Kelly was taking his turn as the lookout man. He should have raised the alarm, organised a rescue plan for Hughie, donned breathing apparatus. Instead he jumped into the granulator, grabbed hold of his companion and bundled him out.

They pulled off Hughie's boots and ran water over his poor burned feet before calling an ambulance.

Forty

Inquiry

The accident inquiry noted five things:

1. Fiona should not have overruled the lead operator
2. The lead operator should not have listened to Fiona
3. The lead operator should not have sent the recycle back to the reactor
4. The lead operator should not have sent men into a granulator that contained liquid
5. Kelly was commended for his rescue

Fiona was disciplined for operating the granulation plant recycle function exactly as it was designed and left the company soon afterwards. The lead operator was disciplined for his lack of foresight in listening to Fiona and told to be more prescient in future. Hughie returned to work six months later but never wore sandals again. Kelly was awarded hero status for not following emergency procedures and everyone bought him drinks at the next Christmas party.

Tenth Clue

OIL CAN

SUPERPHOSPHATE

Forty-one

Aladdin's Lamp

The clock ticks. A thin red hand moves inside a silver rim, progressing smoothly round the moonfaced circle, passing the black numerals on a white face, one by one.

There are two living people in Torphichen Street Police Station Interview Room Number 2: retired factory worker John Gibson and Detective Inspector Rose Irvine. They are looking at a tray that contains the last possessions of a third person, deceased, identity unknown.

'So,' she says. 'Let's see where we are.'

She stares at the tray of objects.

'Fraser Docherty is accounted for.'

Her sleeve slides back as she picks up the nutmeg grater and places it to one side, exposing a bare forearm lightly freckled and dusted in soft pink down. Today her scent has more citrus about it: a woman without brand loyalty.

'These were last seen with Blind Willy...' She moves the elephant and sunglasses onto the table beside the grater. 'But you attended his cremation, and we have his death certificate, which rules him out.'

'Tall Willy is in China looking at steam engines,' she continues. The air horn and key ring join the other three objects.

'Poor Polly McKay drowned. Her bairn was taken into care.' She drapes the flower bullet on the silver chain around the neck of the Barbie doll and slides the legs of the doll through the hole at the top of the grater, forming a silver skirt a little less lustrous than the former platinum ballgown.

'Keith, the design engineer, is on time and budget on another project.' She slips the arm of the doll through the brass washer, giving her an oversized bracelet. 'And any number of men in the SAI received one of these bottles of contraband whisky from Big Stu at some point in their career.' She feeds the hairy string into the empty bottleneck and watches it twirl.

'Which leaves us with this.' She points to the tenth object on the tray.

John reaches into his trouser pocket and removes a clean, ironed, white handkerchief. He shakes it out and uses it to pick up the oilcan from the tray, the fine cotton protecting the table from stains. His fingers stroke the slippy brass, oil still oozing from the hinge of the conical lid. A curved handle curlicues down one side, a long spout extends the length of his forearm, tapering to a narrow, pointed end. An old design, made in the days when craftsmen had time to construct the beautiful as well as practical, when an apprentice project remained with the creator for life. Back in the days when labour was valued. Aladdin's lamp.

John brings the oilcan to his nose. He opens the lid and sniffs. Oil. Burnished metal. And a lingering hint of spice. Something from the East. Clove? Cinnamon? Nothing so sweet. Pepper? Paprika? Not exactly. He sneezes and, in the absence of a clean hanky, surreptitiously moves the back of his free hand towards his nose before remembering the lass in the room, whereupon he takes a paper tissue from the box on the table.

He holds the oilcan up to the light. Dull gold. What did frankincense and myrrh smell like? Rubbing it with his finger, he bends his ear towards it, catching a low harmonic ring. A little buzz of excitement ripples up his spine, goosebumps prickle his skin. They're getting closer. He half expects a genie to emerge from this Aladdin's lamp and provide the answer the police are searching for. As he cleans the oil and grime away, he notices something stamped on the handle. He takes off his glasses and peers at it.

'A number?' He hands it to the detective inspector to decipher.

'98?' she guesses. 'Does that mean anything?'

He shrugs.

'Or initials perhaps,' she adds. 'PB?'

John shivers. Something is tugging at his memory.

His memory, or his conscience?

Forty-two

Unskilled

They called them unskilled men. John always bristled at the lazy language. Some of the most highly skilled men he had ever worked with had been labelled 'unskilled'. Management-speak for someone without paper qualifications. No good 'O' grades in Maths and English, no Highers, no university degrees. No connections. No uncle in the lodge who could sort them out with an apprenticeship as a fitter or sparky or process operator. Men left out, men left over, men who were glad of manual work at the plant.

Labourers like Brodie, who operated the bulldozer in the Granny plant and knew the analysis of every pile of granules and how to blend it so that the end product was always within specification, mixing in the crap and avoiding the hidden bottles of whisky, a man who caught herring from a trawler in the North Sea on his days off and farmed winter wheat in his spare time.

Scaffolders' labourers like Parky who worked in four dimensions, time being of the essence, able to cast one eye up to the leak in the pipework and whip up the optimal access platform in the shortest time while avoiding the acid cascading down. The trained scaffolders and engineers always condemned the scaffold the next day, but by then the pipe joint had been nipped up, wrapped in gaffer tape and the scaffold had served its purpose and was ready to be taken down.

Greasers like Becksy who couldn't communicate with men, but understood machines, able to diagnose an incipient fault by the lightest of touches.

The end began with the closure of the PhoSAI plant. It was the simplest plant of all, just a big pin mixer. Phosphate rock was moistened with sulphuric acid for superphosphate and with phosphoric acid for triple superphosphate. It took a lot of a labour to fill and empty and pack and clean, and the products could be easily copied by anyone with a bucket and stick, and made more cheaply by those with a lax approach to process safety or clean air.

A vigorous new management took the opportunity of the PhoSAI plant closure to carry out a factory reorganisation, snappily titled 'The Way Ahead'.

The first casualties of the reorganisation were the greasers.

When the management consultants advised head office that decentralised maintenance was the way to improve efficiency, head office told the works manager to 'make it so'.

After the predictable over-my-dead-body stand-off, Tall Willy, the chief engineer, was encouraged to take early retirement and the rest of the management team realised that the best way to preserve their own pensions was carry out the recommendations of the management consultants to the letter. They didn't just decentralise maintenance, they transferred maintenance responsibility to the shift teams. A programme of multi-skilling was agreed, with the proviso that graduate engineers from head office would join the shift teams to ensure quality and safety were maintained. Some work would still require a qualified electrician, or a time-served mechanic, but simple tasks like oiling and greasing could be done by anyone.

The job of the greasers had been to carry an oily rag and fetch things. They were not sophisticated or articulate people and certainly didn't count as craftsmen. But they were good at following instructions. Tall Willy, maintenance supremo, had introduced a foolproof system, developed during his time at Stinky Miller's. All the grades of oil and grease were colour-coded and kept in a clean, locked container. One greaser dispensed the fresh oil into cans marked with the appropriate spot of colour and packed grease into the similarly coded grease guns. The other greasers took the oil to the rotating equipment with the matching colour code and listened. They checked the level. If it was low, they added oil. Slowly and carefully. It was never high. They had been taught that too much lubricant could be as bad as, or worse than, too little. Then they went to the chains and pulleys and conveyor sprockets and listened. They cleaned the grease nozzles and injected lumps of white lard or clear jelly from the guns and then cleaned again. They fetched breakfast for the operators who couldn't leave the plant, or new safety boots for the night shift who arrived after the store closed. They ferried information from one end of the factory to the other, even the greaser who couldn't hear or speak.

No one could remember how Becksy got the job or when he started, but he soon became part of the furniture. He learned to lip-read English, or at least the simple slang needed to do his job in the factory. Words like Yoowess to indicate that something was not functioning correctly. The greasers often worked in pairs, and Becksy was always paired with one of the lazier men who let him do all the work but could talk for two. They all knew that he was not the full shilling, but he was a harmless simpleton, good at his job, with the art of melting away into the background so that no one was ever embarrassed into having to invite him for a drink or a social event after work.

When they announced the redundancies, it didn't seem to register with Becksy. He carried on working as before, oblivious to the seething anger all around. It took a while to sort his package out. Without a bank account, personnel had to pay him his redundancy money in cash. He seemed confused by it all. They were kind but firm.

On his last Friday, they patiently explained that he shouldn't come back next week. He nodded and smiled.

Becksy turned up exactly one week later. On Monday they let him wait until the personnel manager came in and showed him the door. He was there again on Tuesday. John was on shift and made him a cup of tea and spoke kindly before sending him away. On Wednesday Blind Willy had a long chat at him. Becksy was back on Thursday and they got Alec to threaten him. He just kept coming back. Every morning he was there at the gate. He began to harass the others coming in to work.

Until the Customs and Excise raid.

After which Becksy never came back.

It took a little while for head office to realise the extent of their mistake in changing the way maintenance was done at the plant. A different person now attended to the routine tasks each day. If a shift was busy, the less critical tasks were skipped, but then those on the following shift topped up the oil until it overflowed. The key to the oil store vanished, and even when the door was jemmied open, no one could be bothered to walk all the way down there, so the lubricants were kept close to the equipment in dirty corners where they collected dust and grit. The colour-coding system got lost and the grades of oil and grease got mixed up.

All this might have been tolerated by the equipment if someone had listened.

More than anything else, the greasers listened. They attended the same machine at the same time every weekday. They learned to recognise the hums and purrs and squeaks of normal operation. They could feel the operating temperature of the motors. They were so finely attuned to any changes in vibration or an increase in heat that they could spot incipient problems well in advance.

Especially Becksy. In fact, the man they called a deaf mute was the best listener of all. He listened with his fingers and had an uncanny knack of spotting when a machine needed attention. The mechanics mocked him behind his back, but if he led them to a gearbox, they knew to take it seriously. Becksy might not know what the problems were, or how to solve them, but if he pointed something out, action would be taken within hours.

Now, no one was listening. When the granulator gearbox finally seized up one cold winter night, it took everyone by surprise. The granulation plant had to be shut down for a month to replace the main bearing and straighten the shaft. Amid the investigations and recriminations, no one could quite agree who to blame.

In the days before the minimum wage, the greasers earned a pittance. The cost to repair the Granny plant in 1988 was £150,000 plus £400,000 in lost production. With a weight of seventy kilograms or 2,250 troy ounces, and a gold price of £250 per ounce in 1988, Becksy had literally been worth his weight in gold[39].

Forty-three

The List

Detective Inspector Rose Irvine drums her fingers against the list. They have exhausted the clues. John has inspected each of the objects found with the body, told her the associated stories. In most cases, he has been able to provide a date and a name. It's not enough.

She hasn't finished yet.

John was very specific about the list he needed. Employees at the factory by year from the date it started to the date it closed.

It sounded simple. Turned out to be anything but.

The factory personnel records had been shredded and sent to landfill. The huge computers at Ravelston – too old and complex to back up, mainframe technology made redundant by the smaller personal computers springing up like mushrooms – were dismantled and sold as scrap. Somewhere in those transistors, bridges, resistors and circuits lay the ones and zeros that made up the history of employment.

All gone.

Finance records were kept long beyond the seven years required by legal statute, the accounts being significantly more important than the people. However, these records proved of little use. Payroll was an armoured van sent down from Ravelston to Leith each Friday. Most shop floor employees were paid weekly, in cash, right up to the day the factory closed its gates. There was a record of the total, but not the names of individuals.

Pensions were paid by a separate company, set up independently of the factory. The police requested the records but were told that they would have to specify a name, as they had done when trying to locate John Gibson. Since a name was what the police didn't have and were trying to find out, they got into a tussle, culminating in a court order to oblige the company to provide all records. Be careful what you wish for. The data dump on over a hundred thousand ex-ICI employees was as good as useless.

The one thing that's never lost is tax. National Insurance paid by both employees and employer on their behalf is recorded in the Scottish tax office and easily searchable by employer reference.

Over a thousand names.

Rose got the list by year, as John had requested, page upon page of computer printout, but then she went further.

First, she eliminated all those who were still actively contributing to the nation's coffers, and therefore alive and well and working somewhere else.

Pitifully few of those.

Next, she eliminated all those who had died. When a person shuffles off his mortal coil he takes his National Insurance number to the grave with him. The state has ways to ensure that no benefits are accidentally paid to the deceased.

She was not surprised at the number of men who died shortly after losing their jobs. She's seen the pattern with her own father, with his friends. Retirement party, the plans for golf/gardening/trainspotting discussed with fake enthusiasm. Even men who professed to hate their jobs, who moaned incessantly at the long hours, the gruelling physical effort, who picked fights with their colleagues, got into trouble with management, loathed every hour that they spent at work, discovered too late that it was what sustained them.

Fit men in their mid-sixties upped and died of sudden heart attacks or succumbed slowly to cancer just when they should be enjoying unlimited lunchtime drinking without fear of John's 'kiss'.

Finally, she eliminated all those in receipt of benefits. A handful of state pensioners, those who hadn't worked at the factory long enough to contract out into the enhanced company scheme, many more in receipt of unemployment benefit or housing benefit or child allowance. All apparently alive and cashing in.

By the time she'd finished with the list there were thirty-two names of people who had neither recent taxable activity nor benefits nor death certificates.

She sent the list to the pension company, requesting the addresses and confirmation of recent activity of those receiving pension payments.

Now that the second list has arrived, she goes to find John.

Forty-four

Bombe Glacée

John waves at Detective Inspector Rose Irvine as she walks through the door of the Italian café in Canonmills. He stands to help her with her coat, pulls out a chair at his table.

She's had the courtesy to ring ahead, has asked Giuseppe to ask John if she can join him for lunch. When John sees the specials board, spots the new dessert options, he rubs his hands together at the prospect of Rose's face lighting up. He is not disappointed.

Rose brings news. The list that John asked for is complete. He is to come to the station when he is ready.

There is something else; he can see her excitement, the slight flush to her cheek when he asks her about forensics.

'Let's eat first,' she says.

They order the specials. *Polpette* followed by *Zuppa de Pesce*, and an ice cream bomb for Rose. A carapace of crisp milk chocolate with a melting interior of ice cream. 'I hear you've been talking to people, asking about me.'

'All part of the job,' she says, unruffled. 'How did you know?'

He taps his long nose. 'I have my sources.'

She nods towards the window, up the hill. 'The lass in Tesco Express?'

'Wee Jackie.' He nods. 'We look out for one another.'

'And others,' she says.

'What did you find out?' he asks.

220

She pauses, then smiles. 'You're a good neighbour. You see people, listen to them. Notice when they are unhappy. Take them gifts. People round here won't have a word said against you. Even if you did something wrong.'

'D'you think I did something wrong?' he asks.

She shakes her head. 'Not any more.'

He looks away. Wishes he could be so sure.

The meatballs arrive and, after the usual theatre with pepperpots and Parmesan, they eat in silence.

He watches her eat, taking quiet pleasure in her pleasure, waiting until she finishes.

'Tell me,' she asks. 'What happened to the SAI after it closed down? They say the whole factory was moved to Ireland.'

John wipes the tomato sauce from his lips and begins to laugh.

Forty-five

Closure

After the sulphuric acid plant and the superphosphate plant, the next plants to close were the remaining acid plants. The wise Senegalese had invested development money from the World Bank to build their own phosphoric acid plants and gain some added value from their rich phosphate deposits. And yet, as so often happens, the market price for phosphoric acid plummeted when the new capacity came on-stream. Excess capacity in the USSR and a fall in demand in the developed world meant that the Senegalese would take a long time to pay off their debt. Tankers of phosphoric acid replaced boats full of powdered phosphate rock in Victoria Dock, but the price was not much different.

The new nitric acid plant had only been running for three years when ICI headquarters decided to shut it down. It had performed well – a modern, efficient plant – but lacked the economies of scale enjoyed by larger units. Designed to produce steam to provide heat and power for the rest of the factory, as the other plants were mothballed, one by one, it became less and less efficient.

The cost of running the nitric acid plants in Leith was far greater than running a few tankers of nitric acid up from Billingham. Various ideas were bounced around as to how to recover some of the investment. Mothball it and wait for better times? Demolish it for scrap? Move it? In the absence of Tall Willy's good sense, the worst idea gained greatest favour.

If anyone suggests to you that it would be a good idea to move a chemical plant from one location to another, then here is what you should say to them.

No.

The accountants looked at the shiny new plant with its £30 million value on their books and went out looking for a buyer. They managed to find another group of accountants not only willing to pay £8 million for the plant, but also willing to come and get it.

Most engineers will be able to tell you that the true cost of a chemical plant breaks down into five parts.

The first part is the engineering design. Every vessel, every valve, every instrument, every connection must be properly designed and specified. This is done by large teams of experienced engineers and designers working in open-plan offices producing reams of paper. Big paper, A1 drawings. Paper is cheap but people cost money, even Keith. This part is invisible and often forgotten but is the key to all projects.

The second part, and the easiest to estimate, is the cost of the main equipment: reactors, pumps, compressors, tanks, columns, condensers, boilers. Lots of bits of shiny metal, easy to see and count and value.

The third part is the civil and mechanical installation: the holes dug in the ground, the piles sinking like the roots of trees, driven down with massive percussive hammers to the same depth as the structures that will rise above them. The metal structures to cradle the columns and the piping to connect everything up. Not forgetting the pipe supports, and high-level vents and low-level drains and removable spools. Finally, the lagging to keep things hot, and the many layers of paint so that the plant beside the sea doesn't rust away.

The fourth part is the electrical instrument and control

system. The motors and cables and sensors. The brain of a plant gets smaller and more agile as computer technology advances. The control system designed three years before a plant is built will be already out of date by the time it is started up.

The fifth part is everything not included above. The cost of new boilers and cooling towers and air compressors and seawater pumps and roads and offices to run the plant, the finance costs of borrowing the money, the in-house project manager, project engineers, construction manager, safety advisors, commissioning team and the operators and maintenance teams who have to be hired long before the plant is running smoothly and making money. The raw materials and utilities for start-up, the disposal and write-off costs of the first material which is out of specification. The diesel generators and hired boilers and Portakabins. The local authority permits and registrations.

A useful rule of thumb, in the absence of better information, is to assume that each of the five parts costs about the same. So, if you know the cost of the main equipment, multiply by five to get the cost of the plant. Of course, there are lots of exceptions: some companies don't include the cost of their own people; if you are designing in the USA and building in China your travel budget will be significantly higher; a manually operated plant won't have much instrumentation. And so on.

All things being equal, the cost of the visible equipment represents about 20 per cent of the final cost of a complex chemical plant.

If the accountants for the buyer had known this useful rule, they would have realised that if they paid £8 million for the equipment, the final cost of a five-year-old plant (by the time it was dismantled, moved and rebuilt) would be about

£40 million, significantly more than a brand new plant. If it really was a small nitric acid plant that they wanted, and it was unclear why, given that the economics would not be any different, they would be better to start from scratch.

However, the idea that they were getting a bargain had taken hold. High politics and career trajectories were tied up in the decision. Many seasoned engineers pointed out the folly of the enterprise and were sidelined. The board approved the deal based on a woeful underestimate of the risk, of the time it would take and the cost of completing it.

The deal was the equivalent of selling the elegant, sunny, south-facing sitting room on the second floor of a prestigious New Town Georgian town house in order to move the space inside it to a modern Belfast duplex.

The nitric acid plant which moved from Leith never ran properly in its new home and was eventually shut down and demolished for scrap. It took many years of haemorrhaging money before the project was abandoned.

The seasoned engineers were vindicated, but it gave them no pleasure. The failure of the venture affected ICI and their pensions.

Rose eats her bombe glacée while John tells her about the disastrous removal. She waits until coffee before telling John her other news.

'Forensics have finally done something useful.'

'About time,' he says.

'They analysed the contents of the oil drums found with the body.'

'The braziers?'

Kelly was right about that. John had reached the same conclusion.

'Guess what the fuel was?'

John shakes his head.

'Nae idea.'

Rose leans forward, triumphant. 'Money.'

'Whit the…?'

'Pound notes, fivers and tenners, even twenty- and fifty-pound notes.'

John stares as her, his mouth opening, forgetting to cover it with his hand.

'That's not all,' she adds.

John leans forward.

'The corpse had liquefied.'

John shudders, grips the table.

'But the new lab managed to evacuate the human remains without damaging the phosphate rock shell.'

The clock ticks.

'It's a perfect mould. They're making a plaster cast of the body.'

Forty-six

Confession

This time it is John who insists on coming to the station. He mounts the stairs to the interview room, two at a time, and has to wait for Rose to catch up.

Rose unlocks the door and points to the table.

'There's your list,' she says.

The computer paper is of a kind John hasn't seen for years. Smooth and shiny, alternate bands of pale green and white run horizontally across the landscape format. Vertical columns of small circular holes, designed to fit the now-obsolete printer's sprockets, form the left and right borders, separated from the printed data by dashed perforations. Each A3 page is connected, zig-zag style, to the next. A single concertina of paper that expands into a continuous list of names.

John sits down, but Rose remains standing. 'Fancy a cup of tea?'

'Aye.'

The detective inspector leaves the room.

John takes his time. Resting his gnarled hands on the smooth paper, he runs long fingers over the indentations and perforations. The list contains the names of employees for each year the Leith fertiliser factory operated from 1955 to 1997.

Pure data analysis has never been John's strength. He always despised managers who sat in their offices poring over sheets of numbers instead of talking to their men. Managers who imagined that shift-workers would leave the warm fug of their control room bothy every hour and climb to the top of an exposed tank to find a dirty, dimly lit pressure gauge and take note of a reading which never varied much.

Masters in pattern recognition and boss psychology, the older hands learned not to write the same number when they falsified the records. They varied it by a point here, a point there; knew to change the handwriting, or the thickness of black biro used. The artists added a smudge of dirt or a smear of grease to complete the illusion that operators paid any attention to what desk-bound managers asked them to do.

John preferred to move, to observe, to talk, to listen, to touch, to taste, to smell. In his experience, tables of data were the dullest reading material of all, but this list is different. It tells an eloquent story of change. He pulls at the pages, letting ones he's read fall, slinky-like, onto to a pile.

Thomson, Robertson, Campbell...

In the early days, almost everyone who worked at the factory was an employee. Good salary, excellent benefits, guaranteed pension. The same surnames appear again and again. Grandfather, uncle, father, brother, cousin, son, nephew, grandson.

Macdonald, Scott, Reid...

The security guards were older men who had laboured in the factory in their prime but could no longer heft a shovel. The telephone exchange was operated by a man who could no longer see. The first canteen staff were the wives and mothers (but rarely the daughters or sisters) of male employees.

Young, Watson, Miller...

Even the craftsmen – the fitters and tiffys, sparkies and riggers, carpenters and welders, laggers and scaffolders

– were full-time employees. The port stevedores were public employees and a law unto themselves. Only the potash drivers were contractors.

Graham, Kerr, Simpson…

Security was the first to be contracted out to private companies. The incumbents took early retirement, disgusted by the change to arrangements. The new gatemen had no experience of factory work. They didn't know to put out a dummy Tannoy call when danger loomed – a manager seen leaving the office in a hard hat and boots. They didn't know the relay codes so that the rigger taking a nap in his cab could be woken before he was caught, the announcement to make when six bottles of whisky were heading over from Sally Street in the granulation conveyor belt.

Grant, Mackenzie, Mackay…

The promised 'efficiency gains' were transparent lies – some private companies were cheaper because they paid their employees less, some because they worked them harder, all because they creamed off the best people to work elsewhere. When maintenance was contracted out, the skilled craftsmen were helicoptered to the North Sea for better-paid oil work, rarely returning to the factory where they had trained.

Muir, Murphy, Johnstone…

An unfamiliar scent rouses John from his reverie. He sniffs at the steam rising from the mug as Rose plonks it on the table beside the computer printout.

'Earl Grey,' she says. 'Is that OK?'

Bergamot. That explains the whiff of citrus and spice.

Once he would have refused such an aberration, mocked anyone who used even Tetley's or PG Tips instead of Lipton's Yellow Label, the original Scottish breakfast tea, tanned the hide of a well-meaning youngster who cleaned out the teapot, destroying years of accumulated flavour from the slightly porous interstices. The choice of tea was a shibboleth, a gang tattoo, a badge of tribe.

He looks down at the stack of computer printout pages. His tribe has been reduced to a list of National Insurance numbers, the print fading before his eyes.

Times have changed. Since his wife died and Beatrice and Giuseppe rescued him from loneliness with a daily lunch in their café, he accepts new flavours with equanimity.

He takes a sip. Good and hot.

'Thanks.' He looks up at her, watches her eyes wrinkle as the smile fades, the way her brows meet with concern. She needn't have done it. Made the tea herself. She could have asked one of the uniforms to do it. This is a woman who understands the power of gesture.

'There's a lot to get through,' she says.

'People,' he replies. 'You have to know their stories.'

As he wonders about her story, she hands him the second list.

'This might help,' she says. 'A cross-check with other data. Employees of the Leith fertiliser factory between 1985 and 1997 with current whereabouts unknown.'

John takes the shorter list of names, puts on his reading glasses and runs a long bony finger down the rows. He turns the page over and reads every name and National Insurance number right to the end before letting it fall to the desk. He wrinkles his brow and looks back at the objects on the tray. He exhales slowly, deeply. As if he will never take another breath. Then his shoulders slump and he bends his head, burying it in his hands as his shoulders shake.

The detective inspector remains silent, watching as John gulps for air at last through his splayed fingers. Is he laughing or crying? He pulls out a handkerchief and blows his nose.

She waits.

'I know who it is.' His voice rasps, as if his throat is dry.

She picks up the list of names. 'Which one? Show me.'

'He's not on either list.'

'So, he didn't work at the factory?'

'Oh, he worked there alright.' John sighs. 'One of the hardest workers I ever knew.'

'Then why isn't he here?' She smacks the paper with the back of her hand.

The noise, like the crack of a whip, makes John jump. His voice falls to a whisper. 'He was paid in his brother's name.'

'I don't understand.'

John shrugs. 'Maybe he didn't have a National Insurance number, so he used his brother's. They paid the men in cash.'

'What was his name?'

John eases the computer printout back to the beginning. 1955. 'Peter Beck.'

She opens her notepad, then hesitates, her pen hovering above the paper. 'The body in the phosphate cave is Peter Beck?'

'No, that was the brother's name.'

'And the victim?'

'He had no name.' John hangs his head. 'We just called him Becksy.'

Big Stu knew that trouble was brewing, he just didn't know when it would arrive.

After a bad pint at the Black Bull (it might have been the ninth or the tenth, he wasn't sure), Ronnie had helped him home. When he woke the following afternoon, he realised he'd left more than his self-respect behind.

Big Stu's list was a double page pulled from the centre of a school exercise jotter, narrow feint lined with four staple-hole eyes in the middle of two A5 wings. It had been creased and folded many times, but the carefully handwritten names of his customers and the dates of their next whisky delivery, in order of eligibility, were still clearly legible. Big Stu might not be scrupulous with data protection, but he was nothing if not fair.

Big Stu called Ronnie. Ronnie had a vague recollection of seeing the list on the table in the Black Bull as Big Stu took new orders. He didn't remember what happened to it after the fight broke out.

Big Stu was waiting outside the door of the Black Bull before evening opening time.

'You've got a nerve,' Brenda said as she served him. 'After last night.'

'Sorry,' Big Stu mumbled, although he wasn't really sure what he was apologising for. 'Did I leave a piece of paper here?'

'What sort of paper?' Brenda narrowed her eyes.

Big Stu described it. 'Customer list,' he added.

Brenda nodded at the makeshift stage where the go-go dancers performed. 'One of them might have taken it.'

'Why?'

'To pay you back.'

'What for?'

'You really don't remember?'

Big Stu tried to recall the previous night, shook his head and then wished he hadn't. 'But what would she want with my list?'

'Present for a friend.'

'What friend?'

'They're all snitches. Friends,' she made elaborate quotation marks with her painted fingernails, 'with the polis. You should be more careful.'

Big Stu swallowed hard and ordered a chaser.

Forty-seven

Police Raid

Big Stu failed to confess the mistake to his customers. He might be careless, but he was not an idiot. On learning that a go-go dancer in the Black Bull had responded to his drunken heckling by passing information to her policeman boyfriend, information that would reveal the names of those buying contraband whisky, his erstwhile clients were unlikely to be understanding. They tended to demonstrate dissatisfaction through the medium of expressive dance, with fists and boots and foreheads.

Big Alec's mates at Leith Police Station got wind of the police raid just before it happened.

'Call for Farquharson,' he announced. 'Can Mr Farquharson please contact the gatehouse.'

The name of the Customs and Excise official from *Whisky Galore!* was enough to galvanise guilty men to action.

Those who had not yet removed their cut-price alcohol from the site set to work. They re-attached the hairy string to the bottle necks and buried the bottles deep under the fertiliser granules in the whalebone sheds.

John left the ammonia spheres compressor room and set off down the factory road as soon as he heard the Tannoy call. He had reached the Nitram plant when the next announcement came.

'Blue alert.'

That meant the police had been spotted entering the docks.

'Repeat, bright blue alert.'

That meant they were close.

John approached the gatehouse from the factory side, just in time to see Blind Willy hand something though the public hatch. Fist-sized, black. Now he thought about it, he must have always known it was the ebony elephant changing hands. Going to a familiar figure on the other side.

'Becksy, you muppet,' John said. 'What are you doing here?'

'He comes every day,' Blind Willy said. 'He doesn't seem to understand. It's breaking my heart.'

'Breaking my balls, more like,' growled Big Alec. 'Fucking spaz.'

Truth was, John missed Becksy, one of the best workers he had ever known. But without Tall Willy and Roderick, both of whom had retired rather than see maintenance decentralised, the rest of management were a bunch of tossers who didn't know one end of a grease gun from the other.

Sympathy wouldn't help Becksy right now.

How to make him understand that he was no longer needed?

John gently moved Blind Willy aside and stuck his head through the hatch, flinching at the way Becksy's face lit up.

Something radical needed to be done. Someone needed to make Becksy understand his job was gone. The greaser might be dumb, but he wasn't stupid. Sometimes you have to be cruel to be kind.

Enough was enough. Threats and insults were water off a duck's back to Becksy. The one thing that Becksy understood was the impartiality of John's laugh. Although never the recipient until now, Becksy had witnessed its effects on others many times.

John sucked his teeth and stretched his lips.

Becksy stepped forward, his lips quivering into a tentative smile.

As John opened his mouth, he pictured Becksy's reaction. First a puzzled frown, his dark monobrow undulating like a bird in flight, then his bottom lip trembling, his eyes moistening, his mouth opening in shock and pain, his heart bursting at the betrayal.

John clamped his mouth shut; he couldn't do it, couldn't force it, couldn't bring himself to deceive a trusted, respected, cherished colleague. Becksy had done everything asked of him, had gone above and beyond, had done nothing to invite mockery and ridicule. John couldn't laugh him away, even if it was for his own good.

Nee-naw, nee-naw!

The siren of the approaching police convoy split the sky. Becksy might not be able to hear the sirens, but he must have seen the flashing blue lights reflected in the window of the gatehouse as the cars and vans sped towards the bridge over Victoria dock.

Big Alec stormed out of the gatehouse and stood between John, with his long face poking through the hatch, and Becksy waiting outside.

The huge gateman nodded towards the approaching police car and then pointed at Becksy before making a handcuffing motion with his hands.

Everyone knew the man was afraid of the police. Terribly afraid.

'No!' John shouted and pulled back through the hatch, banging his jaw on the lip of the hatch as he backed away and strode through the gatehouse, opening the door in time to see Becksy's reaction: frozen on the spot, pupils dilated, skin ghostly pale, limbs trembling.

Their eyes met.

There was a moment, a split second, when John could have rescued the situation, beckoned to Becksy to come inside, reassured the greaser that the police weren't coming for him, that it was Big Stu and his customers they were after. But Big Alec moved between them and the moment passed.

Becksy might be mute, but that didn't stop him emitting a blood-curdling howl as he turned and ran, never to be seen again.

Until now.

Forty-eight

Reconstruction

The reconstruction is ready.

The viewing room is small and sterile – cement floor and tiled walls, sharp angles and smooth surfaces brightly lit from recessed lights in a ceiling that is a little too low. There are two sets of doors in this liminal chamber, interlocked access so that only one can open at a time, portals which connect the living to the dead.

One entrance is for friends and family, connected to a waiting room furnished with easy chairs, a low sofa, and a drinking fountain, all turned away from the wide internal window and door. Through the glass the other entrance can be seen. Double steel doors open wide enough for a gurney to enter from the morgue.

As they bring the body in, the technicians are still marvelling at the way the finely powdered phosphate rock had entered every nook and cranny before setting hard, creating a mould, a negative that preserved the most extraordinary detail. Every bump and hollow, curve and wrinkle is now faithfully recreated in plaster.

A man, aged around sixty at the time of death, sits erect in a chair, his hands on a desk. He is terribly thin: ribs showing though his shirt, hipbones jutting though his trousers, malnourished and dehydrated.

There is stubble on his chin, but his wispy hair is combed neatly across the scalp.

His eyes are wide open, framed by long, thick eyelashes and bushy eyebrows that meet in the middle. He has a full, sensitive mouth and a large, slightly hooked nose.

The ghostly white statue sits under the halogen lights, and waits.

Becksy waits.

No one at the factory knows anything about him: his full name, how old he is, where he is from, whether he has been deaf from birth. Becksy doesn't even know those things himself any more. His colleagues know him as a grafter, someone who pitches in whenever an extra pair of hands are needed. If some make a half-hearted attempt to befriend him, they are soon deterred by the difficulty of communication. That and his refusal to meet outside work. Becksy has never stood a round at the Black Bull, the Freemasons or the Central. In fact, Becksy has never set foot in a pub. Without language, Becksy remains isolated. An island. Tolerated but rarely welcomed. Others find him a bit creepy – his shy smile, his ability to appear from nowhere before melting into the shadows, his silence. They picked on him for a while, but he is an unrewarding target. He doesn't scream when pinched, evinces no disgust when spat or pissed upon. Although he can't answer back and never defends himself, he receives threats and insults, punches and kicks, without reaction. That much his brother taught him. He is often thrashed but never beaten.

Certainly, no one knows where he lives now, the place he calls home. Since arriving from Sevastopol with his older brother, two teenage stowaways on a troop carrier, Becksy has never left Leith docks.

Home is the place where you feel safe.

His brother Petr could hear and speak, read and write, and quickly learned English. The pair found casual work on the docks. The brothers slept in the old granary to save money. It was warm, there was running water, a toilet, a shower and plenty of extra protein to trap if you weren't too squeamish about tails. After Petr got a job at the factory, Becksy assisted, unofficially at first, taking over his brother's role when Petr set off to find something better for both of them.

Becksy tried to leave the dock once, set off to look for Petr, got as far as the police station at the dock gate before he turned tail and fled.

He is terrified of being sent back to Crimea.

When the granary closed, he moved from one place to another. There were miles of tunnels and gangways and warehouses and stores to choose from. In the days when no one cared about energy efficiency, he never lacked for warmth – oversize motors, sloppily clad steam pipes – and the squealing of bearings, clatter of conveyors and hissing of condensate traps didn't bother him. Machines are his friends; the vibration is welcome gossip. *How are you today? Fine, thanks for asking. Those noises you're making, are you in pain? A little unbalanced, if truth be told. I could really use a health check. Let me set that up for you. Why, thanks mate.*

Becksy waits.

He works in the factory as a greaser, the lowest of the low on the bottom rung of factory hierarchy. He washes in the factory amenities block and eats in the factory canteen. Weekends are long and hungry. Building a home under the phosphate elevator takes time, but he is proud of the comfortable nest he constructs from found materials and the ingenious trapdoor he devises, invisible from the machine room above. At first, he keeps his new home clean, brushing away the phosphate rock that spills from the bucket elevator and trickles though the trapdoor above his head.

Despite giving it away whenever he can, Becksy has amassed a small fortune in cash. He has nowhere to spend it now he can no longer access the factory canteen or barter with his colleagues.

He stays close to the factory, for where else would he go? They may not let him inside the gate, but the true factory extends far outside its boundary fence, tendrils of pipe and cable, arteries of conveyor and walkway, down to the docks and into his heart.

He doesn't understand why they won't let him back inside. There is work that needs doing, machines that need regular attendance. He keeps going back. He has to go back. After all, one day Petr will come for him, just like he promised. And how will they find one another if he isn't here? Becksy lives to work. The deaf and dumb Ukrainian who is worth his weight in gold is worthless without a job.

He collects broken things and finds ways to mend them, telling himself the stories of the factory to distract from the hunger gnawing at his belly. As the first frost bites, he burns the last of his redundancy money to keep warm, propping the trapdoor slightly open to release the smoke.

When he becomes too weak from starvation to climb the ladder, he arranges his favourite objects in order.

Becksy waits.

Author's Note

After completing a Master's degree in Chemical Engineering at Cambridge University, England, I returned home to Edinburgh, Scotland, and my first graduate job. Employed by SAI, Scottish Agricultural Industries, from 1983 to 1988, for the last two years I worked a continuous twelve-hour shift pattern in the Leith Fertiliser Works.

John Gibson, an experienced and well-respected foreman, became my chaperone and mentor, and remains a firm friend. Now approaching his nineties, he has given his blessing for a fictionalised account of our workplace adventures. The Leith factory closed in the 1990s and was demolished a few years later.

In 1988 I was offered a new job with a fine chemical company in Portugal. I agreed to stay on shift at SAI until the start of a planned maintenance shutdown. When I drove down Leith Walk on my Honda 90 in 1988 and saw that there was no steam coming out of the chimneys, I knew it was my last shift.

All – except one – of the events described in *Phosphate Rocks* took place during my working life as a chemical engineer, although not necessarily in the same place, to the same people or in the same order described in *Phosphate Rocks*.

The anecdote of the deaf man – a refugee from behind the iron curtain – who was too scared to leave the docks was told to me by one of the Leith stevedores. I have never been able to find firm evidence to back it up, but the story stuck with me and became the framework for *Phosphate Rocks*.

More than one dead body was fished out of the water during my time at Leith. Outside of the factory, it was a dangerous place to walk at night.

Inside, too.

An accident at work led to a man being engulfed in acid after he hit a lead pipe with a hammer. He returned to work in the gatehouse, blind and badly scarred, to operate the telephone exchange and Tannoy.

Another accident at work led to a man's feet being scalded after he entered a vessel containing a hidden, boot-high layer of boiling liquid under a solid crust.

The trade in contraband whisky from the bonded warehouse on Salamander Street was stamped out after a police investigation; no one is quite sure what happened to the evidence the policemen seized.

I have tried to be true to the spirit of the Leith Fertiliser Works, even as I have fictionalised the characters and the stories.

I have spent time in many factories with many fine people over my working life, but the motley crew I worked with at SAI will always have a special place in my heart.

Acknowledgements

This book would never have seen the light of day were it not for my husband, Jonathan Erskine, who encouraged me to curb my wild escape into fiction for long enough to write down some true stories from my professional life.

My appreciation and thanks go to my work colleagues at SAI and elsewhere for providing so much rich source material, in particular to my lifelong friend John Gibson.

While working shifts at SAI, I had a lot of free time. I volunteered at the Edinburgh Deaf Club on Albany Street and met Pat McLaughlin who had decided, on retiring from a lifetime of hard manual work, that it was time to learn how to read and write. I was assigned to help, but learned a great deal more from Pat than he ever learned from me. Pat and his wife Monica, both profoundly deaf from birth, had attended a school which forbade the use of sign language, a cruelty that is almost unimaginable today. I had never fully appreciated how isolating it is to be deaf and deprived of your natural language.

Thanks to NaNoWriMo, a non-profit organization that encourages creativity through free writing; to Debi Alper, my first writing teacher and constant guide who encouraged me to turn a set of sketches into a novel; Lydia Syson, who read an early draft and gave me valuable advice on how to pitch it; Sarah Armstrong, who, despite reading a raw version, gave me a massive confidence boost; my clever sister Helen

Macleod for eagle-eyed reading and encouragement; Dr Ivan Vince for checking my chemistry and calculations (all residual errors are mine!); and last but not least the fantastic team at Sandstone Press, with special thanks to my editor Robert Davidson.

People

i. **Jabir ibn Hayyan (721–815)**

The father of chemistry, Jabir was an eighth-century natural philosopher and experimental chemist who lived in Persia and Iraq. He wrote many books in Arabic, providing the first systematic classification of chemical substances and documenting the oldest known instructions for making inorganic chemical compounds (such as ammonium chloride) from living things. His Latinised name (Geber) may also be the origin of the word gibberish (incomprehensible technical jargon) as his work was written in highly esoteric code to ensure that only those who had been initiated into his alchemical school could understand it.

ii. **Katherine Jones, Lady Ranelagh (1615–1691)**

Katherine was the seventh of fifteen children. She was betrothed at nine, married at fifteen and bore four children before escaping from war in Ireland and an unhappy marriage to set up an independent life in London. Together with little brother Robert Boyle, she embarked on 'a lifelong intellectual partnership, where brother and sister shared medical remedies, promoted each other's scientific ideas, and edited each other's manuscript'. They made a wish list of twenty-four inventions including the 'art of flying', 'perpetual light', 'making armour light and extremely hard', 'a ship to sail with all winds' without sinking, 'practicable and certain way of finding longitudes', 'potent drugs to... appease pain'[1].

iii. **Robert Boyle (1627–1691)**

Robert was a seventeenth-century chemist, born into a wealthy family and free to pursue scientific interests. The fourteenth of fifteen children, he never married but formed an intellectual partnership with his brilliant older sister, Katherine Jones. He visited Galileo Galilei in Italy in 1641 to gaze at stars and ponder the paradoxes of the universe. He hired brilliant polymath Robert Hooke (1634–1703) as his laboratory assistant and contributed to the founding of the Royal Society in 1662. One of the pioneers of the modern experimental scientific method, he proved that the absolute pressure of a gas is inversely proportional to its volume (Boyle's Law).

iv. **Hennig Brand (1630–1710)**

The last of the alchemists, Henning discovered the chemical element phosphorus in 1669 while searching for the 'philosopher's stone', a catalyst to turn base metals into gold. He married twice.

v. **John Roebuck of Kinneil (1718–1794)**

John was an inventor and industrialist who developed a process for industrial-scale manufacture of sulphuric

1. DiMeo, Michelle, '"Such a sister became such a brother": Lady Ranelagh's influence on Robert Boyle', in special Boyle issue of *Intellectual History Review*, 25 (2015), 21–36.

acid using rectangular wooden chambers lined with lead. He trained as a medical doctor in Edinburgh and Leiden, but his passion was for chemistry.

vi. **Antoine Lavoisier (1743–1794)**
Antoine was a French nobleman, tax collector and scientist. He proved the role played by oxygen in combustion and changed chemistry from a qualitative (descriptive) to quantitative science with his passions for accurate measurement. He worked for the private tax-collecting arm of the French government (Ferme Générale) as gunpowder administrator, where his interest in chemistry blossomed and he was able to construct a state-of-the-art chemistry laboratory. He married Marie-Anne Pierrette Paulze and his wife assisted with his scientific research, translating scientific papers and actively participating in her husband's laboratory work. At the height of the Reign of Terror during the French Revolution, he was accused of tax fraud, convicted and executed by guillotine. He was later completely exonerated.

vii. **Marie-Anne Pierrette Paulze (1758–1836)**
Marie-Anne was three years old when she was sent to a convent on the death of her mother. Married at the age of thirteen to Antoine Lavoisier (then aged twenty-eight) to avoid a union with a much older man at her father's workplace, the Ferme Générale, Marie-Anne became her husband's lab assistant, translator and illustrator. Her husband and father fell afoul of the French Revolution and were both executed by guillotine on the same day in 1794. She remarried in 1804, to

the American-born physicist Sir Benjamin Thompson, Count Rumford, but the second marriage was not a happy one and they separated after three years.

viii. **Alexander von Humboldt (1769–1859)**
The first person to identify human-induced climate change, Alexander was a Prussian explorer, botanist and geographer who travelled the world and published thirty volumes of beautifully illustrated observations. Together with his friend Joseph Louis Gay-Lussac, he made water from hydrogen and oxygen. He never married.

ix. **Jane Marcet (née Haldimand) (1769–1858)**
Jane wrote and illustrated popular science books, 'Conversations', that were both accessible and scientifically accurate. One of twelve children born to a Swiss banker in London, she was educated with her brothers and took over the running of the household and her father's scientific and literary soirées from the age of fifteen when her mother died. She published *Conversations on Chemistry* anonymously in 1803. It was based on Humphry Davy's public lectures and was to have a profound effect on Michael Faraday. She married a doctor and they set up a chemical laboratory at their home in London. She had four children.

x. **Humphry Davy (1778–1829)**
Humphry was a British chemist and the father of electrochemistry. He perfected a safety lamp for Cornish miners and identified several chemical elements:

potassium, sodium, calcium, strontium, barium, magnesium, and chlorine. He was a brilliant scientific communicator, appointed as a chemistry lecturer to the newly created Royal Institution at the age of twenty-two. An incorrigible experimenter, he took enormous personal risk. Almost asphyxiating himself with nitrous oxide (which he named laughing gas), he became temporarily blind while preparing nitrogen trichloride, but it didn't teach him any lessons about safety. His laboratory assistant, Michael Faraday, took over preparation and both suffered another accident when the explosive... exploded. He was a supporter of women's education, married once and had no children.

xi. **Joseph Louis Gay-Lussac (1778–1850)**
Amateur balloonist Joseph was a French scientist with professorships in both chemistry and physics. He improved the design of lead chambers for the manufacture of sulphuric acid by adding packing and cooling. He proved that gas pressure increases with temperature, discovered the chemical elements boron and iodine, developed pipettes and burettes and carried out many experiments with alcohol and water to develop the 'degrees Gay-Lussac' scale. It's a tough job, but someone has to do it. He married once and had five children.

xii. **Peregrine Phillips (1800–1888)**
Peregrine was a vinegar merchant who improved the manufacture of sulphuric acid with the invention of the new contact process.

xiii. **Michael Faraday (1791–1867)**

Michael discovered and applied the underlying principles of electromagnetism and electrolysis and founded the Royal Society Christmas Lectures in 1825. The son of a blacksmith, he received almost no formal education and never developed his mathematical abilities beyond basic algebra and trigonometry. Despite these humble beginnings, Michael became one of the most influential scientists in history, laying the groundwork for James Clerk Maxwell, Albert Einstein and Ernest Rutherford. While apprenticed to a bookbinder he read the popular science books of Jane Marcet and became fascinated with science. He approached Davy and was taken on as an assistant. Eschewing worldly ambition and material riches, he turned down the offer of a knighthood and would not stand as president of the Royal Institution. He refused to advise the British Government on the production of chemical weapons for the Crimean War on ethical grounds. He married once and had no children.

xiv. **Amelia Joule, née Grimes (1814–1854)**

I wish I knew more about Amelia. History only records that she was the daughter of the Liverpool Comptroller of Customs and, aged thirty-three, married James Prescott Joule. They had three children. She died aged forty, along with her youngest child, shortly after giving birth. Life was pretty rubbish for Victorian women and infants.

xv. **James Prescott Joule (1818–1889)**

James Prescott Joule was a British scientist who

discovered the relationship between heat and work which led to the first law of thermodynamics and the principle of conservation of energy. Joule's gravestone is inscribed with the number 772.55, the mechanical equivalent of heat. In 1878 he showed by experiment that the same amount of energy is required to lift 772.5 pounds weight by one foot as is required to heat one pound of water by one degree Fahrenheit. In other words, the amount of mechanical work necessary to raise the temperature of one kilogram of water by one degree Celsius is the same as it takes to lift 427 kilograms by one metre. He famously invited Lord Kelvin on his honeymoon after marrying Amelia Grimes. James and Amelia had three children.

xvi. **William Thomson, 1st Baron Kelvin, (1824–1907)**
The first British scientist to be elevated to the House of Lords, William was a physicist and telegraph engineer who helped to formulate the first and second laws of thermodynamics and unified physics as we know it today. He joined James Prescott Joule and his new wife Amelia on honeymoon. He married twice. After his first wife died, he bought a schooner, *Lalla Rookh*, and took to the sea. He proposed to his second wife by telegraph as he approached Funchal harbour in Madeira. Fortunately, she was proficient in morse code, and accepted.

xvii. **Carl Friedrich Claus (1827–1900)**
Carl was a German-born British chemist. He invented a process to recover high purity sulphur from hydrogen sulphide gas. He married twice and had five children.

xviii. **Herman Frasch (1851–1914)**

Herman was a German-born American chemist and mining engineer. He invented a process for fractional distillation of crude oil with the removal of sulphur. In the process named after him (Frasch process), he used superheated water to melt sulphur deposits underground and bring it to the surface as liquid. He married twice and had two children.

xix. **Wilhelm Ostwald (1853–1932)**

Wilhelm was a Latvian-born German chemist and philosopher who invented a commercial process for making nitric acid. He also made key contributions to the understanding of chemical equilibria (how far), kinetics (how fast), catalysis, crystallisation, atomic theory and Esperanto. He married and had five children.

xx. **Booker Taliaferro Washington (1856–1915)**

Booker T. was an African American born into slavery. He was freed from a plantation aged nine and worked in salt furnaces and coal mines, teaching himself to read and write and progressing to a black college, going on to lead a university. He visited Europe, including the sulphur mines of Sicily in 1910. He became the leading voice of former slaves and their descendants, championing black progress through education and entrepreneurship. He married three times and had three children.

xxi. **Fritz Haber (1868–1934)**

The inventor of a process to fix nitrogen and 'make bread from air', Fritz also led a team perfecting the manufacture and deployment of chemical weapons. He married Clara Immerwahr and they had one son, Hermann, who at the age of twelve witnessed his mother's slow death from a self-inflicted gun injury (Hermann later died by suicide himself). Fritz married again and had two further children, but the marriage broke up. He escaped from Nazi Germany in 1933 but was not readily accepted outside Germany and died in Switzerland, impoverished and alone.

xxii.   **Clara Immerwahr (1870–1915)**
Clara Immerwahr was a German chemist, the first German woman to be awarded a doctorate in chemistry. She married Fritz Haber in 1901 but shot herself in 1915 in protest at his work with chemical weapons. She had one child.

xxiii. **Carl Bosch (1874–1940)**
Carl was a German chemical engineer. As an employee of BASF, he was responsible for scaling up Fritz Haber's process to obtain full-scale manufacture of ammonia. This involved finding the right catalyst, designing materials and equipment that could withstand the high pressures and temperatures and purifying the feedstock (hydrogen and nitrogen) and the product ammonia. He married once and had two children.

xxiv.   **Robert Le Rossignol (1884–1976)**
Robert Le Rossignol was a British chemist who worked with Fritz Haber on the Haber-Bosch process. He was interned in Germany in 1914 at the outbreak of the First World War, returning to Britain at the end of the

war. He married and had two children, both of whom he outlived.

xxv. **Dan Flavin (1933–1996)**
Dan Flavin was an American minimalist artist who created installations using coloured fluorescent light. He designed the artworks for specific gallery spaces, creating bespoke light and shade. *'monument' for V. Tatlin* was an exhibition in homage to Vladimir Tatlin, a Russian sculptor: 'the great revolutionary, who dreamed of art as science'. In order to preserve twentieth-century artworks, curators and conservators have to make decisions about authenticity and obsolescence, artistic intent and interpretation. The original, energy-inefficient fluorescent tubes are no longer made. Modern conservationists must make difficult decisions about how to maintain the works. Or not.

Processes

A. Claus Process (1893) – Manufacture of sulphur

Hydrogen sulphide gas reacts with oxygen to give solid sulphur and water.

$$2H_2S_{(g)} + O_{2\ (g)} \rightarrow S_{2\ (s)} + 2\,H_2O_{\ (l)}$$

A1. First step – Hydrodesulphurisation of oil

Organo-sulphur compounds (found in coal, oil and gas) react with hydrogen to give hydrogen sulphide gas, for example with ethanethiol.

$$C_2H_5SH + H_2 \rightarrow C_2H_6 + H_2S$$

A2. Second step – Burn in restricted air

Hydrogen sulphide gas is fed to a furnace and burnt with a restricted amount of air so that only one third is oxidised to sulphur dioxide.

$$2\,H_2S + 3\,O_2 \rightarrow 2\,SO_2 + 2\,H_2O$$

A3. Third Step – Catalytic reduction

The sulphur dioxide and hydrogen sulphide continue over a catalyst bed of titanium dioxide or activated alumina and react to form sulphur, which is condensed and removed as a liquid, then solidified.

$$4 H_2S + 2 SO_2 \rightarrow 3 S_2 + 4 H_2O$$

B. Contact Process (1831) – Manufacture of sulphuric acid
Solid sulphur is burned in air and dissolved in water to give sulphuric acid.

$$2S_{(solid)} + O_{2\,(gas)}\ 2H_2O_{(liquid)} \rightarrow 2 H_2SO_{4\,(liquid)}$$

But, as ever, I think you'll find it's a little more complicated than that...

B1. First step – sulphur to sulphur dioxide
Solid sulphur is melted and burned to produce sulphur dioxide gas.

$$S_{(solid)} + O_{2\,(gas)} \rightarrow SO_{2\,(gas)}$$

B2. Second step – sulphur dioxide to sulphur trioxide
Sulphur dioxide gas is oxidised to sulphur trioxide over a solid vanadium pentoxide catalyst.

$$2 SO_{2\,(gas)} + O_{2\,(gas)} \rightarrow 2 SO_{3\,(gas)} \text{ (in presence of } V_2O_5)$$

B3. Third step – sulphur trioxide to oleum
Sulphur trioxide is dissolved in concentrated sulphuric acid to form oleum.

$$H_2SO_{4\,(liquid)} + SO_{3\,(gas)} \rightarrow H_2S_2O_{7\,(liquid)}$$

B4. Fourth step – oleum plus water to sulphuric acid

Oleum is diluted with water to form sulphuric acid.

$$H_2S_2O_{7 \text{ (liquid)}} + H_2O_{\text{ (liquid)}} \rightarrow 2\, H_2SO_{4 \text{ (liquid)}}$$

C. Manufacture of phosphoric acid

Phosphoric acid is made by reacting phosphate rock with a strong acid. Hydrogen from sulphuric acid H_2SO_4 swaps places with calcium in the rock giving solid calcium sulphate called gypsum – and liquid phosphoric acid. A filter then separates the solids from the liquid.

C1. Wet process

Phosphate rock (fluorapatite $(3Ca_3(PO_4)2.CaF_2)$) containing calcium hydroxyapatite and calcium carbonate is mixed with sulphuric acid to give phosphoric acid, gypsum and water.

$$Ca_3(PO_4)_{2 \text{ (solid)}} + 3H_2SO_{4 \text{ (aqueous)}} \rightarrow 2H_3PO_{4 \text{ (aqueous)}} + 3CaSO_{4 \text{ (solid)}}$$

$$CaCO_{3 \text{ (solid)}} + H_2SO_{4 \text{ (aqueous)}} \rightarrow CaSO_{4 \text{ (solid)}} + H_2O_{\text{ (liquid)}} + CO_{2 \text{ (gas)}}$$

Side reactions with Calcium fluoride give Hexafluorosilicic acid.

$$3CaF_{2 \text{ (solid)}} + SiO_{2 \text{ (solid)}} + 3H_2SO_{4 \text{ (liquid)}} \rightarrow H_2SiF_{6 \text{ (liquid)}} + 3CaSO_{4 \text{ (solid)}} + 2H_2O_{\text{ (liquid)}}$$

The reaction conditions determine the crystal structure of the gypsum, which in turn determines the ease of filtration. Gypsum crystals come in the form dihydrate

$CaSO_4.2H_2O$, α-hemihydrate $CaSO_4.1/2H_2O$ or anhydrite $CaSO_4$. Lower temperatures favour the dihydrate but at higher temperatures the hemihydrate is produced.

The gypsum is removed by filtration and the acid is concentrated using vacuum distillation.

D. Haber-Bosch Process – Ammonia

The revolutionary process that allows humans to fix nitrogen in air was the brainchild of Fritz Haber[xxi] and Karl Bosch[xxiii].

$$N_{2\ (g)} + 3H_{2\ (g)} \rightarrow 2NH_{3\ (l)}$$

D1. First step – Nitrogen production

To separate nitrogen from air, you first filter the air to remove dust, and then cool it in stages until it reaches -200°C. As the air cools, the water vapour condenses, and you remove it using absorbent filters. Carbon dioxide freezes at -79°C and you remove it as a solid. Oxygen and nitrogen liquefy between minus 183°C and -196°C. You recover the nitrogen from the liquid air mixture by fractional distillation. Different substances have different boiling points and you choose the number of distillation plates (boiling and condensing stages) to get the purity required.

D2. Second step – Hydrogen production

Hydrogen can be made by splitting water using electrolysis.

$$2H_2O \rightarrow O_2 + 2H_2$$

But for economic reasons, most hydrogen is made from natural gas (methane) and steam.

$$CH_4 + 2H_2O \rightarrow CO_2 + 4H_2$$

There are several sub-steps:

D2.1. Desulphurisation

Natural gas comes from plants, and plants (and the bacteria which help break them down) contain sulphur, so part of the product hydrogen must be recycled to the start of the process in order to hydrogenate the sulphur-containing organic compounds.

$$H_{2\,(gas)} + RSH \rightarrow RH + H_2S_{(gas)}$$

Where R is an organic group like C_2H_5
The hydrogen sulphide produced is passed through beds of zinc oxide where it is converted to solid zinc sulphide.

$$H_2S + ZnO \rightarrow ZnS + H_2O$$

Or using the Claus process, recovered as solid sulphur.

$$2H_2S + 3O_2 \rightarrow 2SO_2 + 2H_2O$$
$$4H_2S + 2SO_2 \rightarrow 3S_2 + 4H_2O$$

D2.2. Steam reforming

The sulphur-free methane is mixed with high- pressure steam and passed over a bed of nickel catalyst to produce syngas (hydrogen plus carbon monoxide). This step is called steam reforming.

$$CH_4 + H_2O \rightarrow CO + 3H_2$$

The steam reforming reaction is endothermic – heat is required – so some of the methane feedstock has to be burnt to provide the energy input, increasing speed of reaction and conversion.

D2.3. Water-gas shift

The next step, the water-gas shift reaction, is exothermic – heat is given out. That means higher temperatures drive a faster reaction, but incomplete conversion. The overall water-gas shift reaction converts the carbon monoxide to carbon dioxide and more hydrogen.

$$CO + H_2O \rightarrow CO_2 + H_2$$

In order to take advantage of both the thermodynamics (conversion) and the kinetics (speed) of the reaction, industrial-scale water-gas shift reactions are conducted in multiple stages consisting of a high temperature shift (HTS) followed by a low temperature shift (LTS) with intermediate cooling.

D2.3.1. High temperature shift

The first (HTS) stage takes place over an iron oxide–chromium oxide catalyst. The reaction is fast but results in incomplete conversion of carbon monoxide. To increase hydrogen production, the gases exiting the high-temperature reactor are cooled and fed to the second lower temperature (LTS) stage.

D2.3.2. Low temperature shift

The LTS catalyst is copper-based and extremely sensitive to sulphur, so as well as cooling, the gases pass through a guard bed of metal oxides to trap any cheeky little elfin wisps of sulphur that snuck past earlier.

D2.3.3. Heat exchange
The heat removed between the high temperature and low temperature reactors, along with the energy in the gases leaving the process, is used to heat the incoming feedstock.

D2.4. Carbon dioxide removal
The carbon dioxide is separated from the hydrogen by bubbling it through an amine solution (like MEA = monoethanolamine C_2H_7NO) or by pressure swing absorption where the cooled gases pass through beds of absorbent materials which preferentially mop them up. Once the absorption bed is exhausted, the pressure is reduced and the carbon dioxide is released.

D2.5. Catalytic methanation
Hydrogen is used to remove any leftover traces of carbon monoxide or carbon dioxide and protect the ammonia catalyst.

$$CO + 3H_2 \rightarrow CH_4 + H_2O$$
$$CO_2 + 4H_2 \rightarrow CH_4 + 2H_2O$$

D3. React nitrogen and hydrogen of the correct purity to make ammonia
The Haber-Bosch process forward reaction

$$3H_2 + N_2 \rightarrow 2NH_3$$

is in equilibrium with the reverse reaction

$$2NH_3 \rightarrow 3H_2 + N_2$$

It needs special process conditions to drive the forward reaction at acceptable speed and yield. And a catalyst (which you prepared earlier…)

D4. Magnetite catalyst

Don't you hate recipes where you chop the onions and fry them with the ground spices and then you turn the page and it says 'now take the meat that you have previously marinated for 24 hours…'? Maybe I should have mentioned the catalyst first. Just checking to see if you're still paying attention!

The catalyst for the Haber-Bosch process consists of finely ground particles: each particle has a core of magnetite (Fe_3O_4), encased in a shell of wüstite (FeO), which in turn is surrounded by an outer shell of iron metal (Fe). Tremendous skill in preparation leads to a highly porous high-surface-area catalyst. One of Carl Bosch's assistants ran over 20,000 experiments to find the perfect catalyst. He discovered that a commonly available iron ore called magnetite could be used to create a catalyst that worked every bit as well as the expensive (and unstable) osmium-uranium catalyst proposed by Fritz Haber in his original patent. The catalyst is key to the process, and yet Alwin Mittasch (1869–1953) rarely gets a mention.

E. Ostwald Process – Nitric acid

Wilhelm Ostwald[xix] gave his name to the Ostwald process.

E1. First step
Ammonia plus oxygen gives nitric oxide and water.

$$4\,NH_{3\,(g)} + 5\,O_{2\,(g)} \rightarrow 4\,NO_{(g)} + 6\,H_2O_{(l)}$$

E2. Second step
The nitric oxide is reacted with air to form nitrogen dioxide.

$$2\,NO_{(g)} + O_{2\,(g)} \rightarrow 2\,NO_{2\,(g)}$$

E3. Third step
The nitrogen dioxide is bubbled through water to form nitric acid and nitric oxide.

$$3\,NO_{2\,(g)} + H_2O_{(l)} \rightarrow 2\,HNO_{3\,(aq)} + NO_{(g)}$$

The extra nitric oxide is sent back to step E2.

F. Ammonium nitrate
First take ammonia (Haber-Bosch process) and add concentrated nitric acid (from the Ostwald process). Add together and stand well back.

$$HNO_{3\,(aq)}\,(+H_2O) + NH_{3\,(g)} \rightarrow NH_4NO_{3\,(s)}\,(+H_2O)$$

Like many reactions of acids (nitric acid) and alkalis (ammonia) to make a salt (ammonium nitrate), this is a violently exothermic reaction, which means a lot of heat is generated. This heat can be used to evaporate the incoming liquid ammonia and heat the salt solution (~80%

ammonium nitrate in water), evaporating the residual water to obtain an ammonium nitrate melt (>95% ammonium nitrate). The melt is pumped through a shower head at the top of a spray tower. The melt cools and solidifies in air to make 'prills' or small beads. The prills are dried, cooled, and coated to stop them sticking together.

G. The SAI Grande Paroisse granulation process

At the Leith plant, the solid raw materials trundled up a belt and dropped in at one end of the granulator. Liquid ammonia squirted into the moving bed through four huge pokers, sparging into a bed of rolling solids and invariably choking. A hydraulic ram was used to raise the spargers from the bed when not in use, and a parallel steam supply attempted to blast them clear – without much success. Joining the solid raw materials – potash, limestone, superphosphate – came the liquids from the pipe reactors. Liquid ammonium nitrate, a molten, colourless, boiling liquid, was formed by the vigorous reaction between ammonia and nitric acid in a ten-metre-long pipe reactor. A shorter, thinner pipe reactor produced di-ammonium phosphate slurry from ammonia and phosphoric acid. Scrubber liquor was added, recycling the dust and any stray ammonia as a spray of fine droplets directly into the granulator, along with the recycled fines and crushed oversize, and dust collected from the cyclones and filters. The granulator discharged though a chute to the drier. The ideal material was moist, but crisp and glistening, with an equal range of fines (below 2.4 millimetres), product and oversize (above four millimetres). The final process stream was the drier pipe reactor, which mixed ammonia and phosphoric acid and blasted out a fine dust of monoammonium phosphate into the drier, aiding the overall heat balance. The drier was heated with air which passed through a steam heat exchanger. The moisture and dust driven off from the granular material was sucked by the drier fan and passed through cyclones to a venturi before entering the scrubber where it joined the dust and moisture from the granulator. The mopped-up effluent became the scrubber liquor which was carried back to the process in a dispersion of dilute phosphoric acid.

Chemistry, Calculations, Units and Quotes

1. Chemical elements in the human body

Element	Symbol	Percentage (weight)	Weight in grams (g) in 70kg person
Oxygen	O	65.0%	45,500
Carbon	C	18.5%	12,950
Hydrogen	H	9.5%	6,650
Nitrogen	N	3.2%	2,240
Calcium	Ca	1.5%	1,050
Phosphorus	P	1.0%	700
Potassium	K	0.4%	280
Sulphur	S	0.3%	210
All others		0.6%	420

Assuming an average weight of 70kg and assuming 0.3% sulphur, the weight of sulphur in the human body is 210g.

Most phosphorus (P, molecular weight 31) is found in the body in the form of hydroxyapatite

$(Ca_{10} (PO_4)_6 (OH)_2$, molecular weight 1005). If the weight of elemental phosphorus is 700g then there will be (1005/(6x31) x 700 = 3782 grams) 3.782 kg of hydroxyapatite.

Assuming an average weight of 70kg and assuming 0.4% potassium, the weight of potassium in the human body is 280g.

2. Pyrites – iron sulphide, FeS

3. Cinnabar – mercury sulphide, HgS

4. Galena – lead sulphide, PbS

5. Stibnite – antimony sulphide, Sb_2S_3

6. Sphalerite – zinc sulphide, (Zn, Fe)S

7. Gypsum – calcium sulphate, $CaSO_4.2H_2O$

8. Alunite – potassium aluminium sulphate, $KAl_3(SO_4)_2(OH)_6$

9. Barite – barium sulphate, $BaSO_4$

10. Sicilian sulphur mines
    Conditions in the mines of Sicily shocked even those used to the brutal treatment of working men
    Phillip Carroll, U.S Consul, Palermo, 'United States Consular Reports. Special Issue No. 10,' accessed May 20 2020, http://lateralscience.blogspot.com/2018/04/sulphur-mines-in-sicily-1888.html.

11. Washington & Park, The Man Farthest Down.

12. Hydroxyapatite – Calcium phosphate – $Ca_5(PO_4)_3OH$, $(Ca_{10} (PO_4)_6 (OH)_2)$

13. Fluorapatite – Calcium fluorophosphate – $Ca_5(PO_4)_3F$

14. DNA – Deoxyribonucleic acid

15. RNA – Ribonucleic acid

16. ATP – Adenosine tri-phosphate – $C_{10}H_{16}N_5O_{13}P_3$

17. ADP – Adenosine di-phosphate – $C_{10}H_{15}N_5O_{10}P_2$

18. Rubisco is Ribulose-1,5-bisphosphate carboxylase/oxygenase

19. Carbon fixation – plants convert carbon dioxide in the air and water in the ground into sugars using energy from sunlight. The first major step is carboxylation of ribulose-1,5-bisphosphate

20. Guano Islands Act, USA, 1856

21. President Franklin D. Roosevelt, message to Congress, 1938

22. Chitin – $C_8H_{13}O_5N$

23. Mercaptans and Thiols
    The term mercaptan comes from the Latin mercurium captāns (capturing mercury) because the thiolate group (RS−) bonds very strongly with mercury compounds.
    Thiols are the sulphur analogue of alcohols where sulphur takes the place of oxygen in the hydroxyl group/ The word is a portmanteau of 'thio-' + 'alcohol', with the first word deriving from Greek θεῖον (theion) meaning 'sulphur'.

24. Furfuryl mercaptan – C_5H_6OS

25. Grapefruit mercaptan – $C_{10}H_{18}S$

26. Tertiary butyl mercaptan – $(CH_3)_3CSH$

27. Potassium compounds in potash can include:

KOH – Caustic potash (Potassium hydroxide)
K_2CO_3 – Potassium carbonate
$KClO_3$ – Potassium chlorate
KCl – Muriate of potash (Potassium chloride)
KNO_3 – Saltpetre (Potassium nitrate)
K_2SO_4 – Potassium sulphate
$KMnO_4$ – Potassium permanganate

28. Davy's(x) accident with nitrogen trichloride didn't teach him any lessons about safety. His new assistant, Faraday(xiii), took over preparation and both suffered another accident when it exploded.

29. Group 1 metals in order of increasing reactivity are lithium, sodium, potassium, rubidium, caesium and francium.

30. The total weight of seawater on planet earth is about 1.4 Quintillion tonnes (1.4×10^{18})
Potassium makes up about 0.04% of seawater so ($1.4 \times 0.04/100 \times 10^{18} = 560 \times 10^{12}$) 560 trillion tonnes.
Using the short scale:
1 trillion = one followed by 12 zeros = 1,000,000,000,000 written as 10^{12}
1 Quadrillion = 10^{15}
1 Quintillion = 10^{18}

31. Claudia Flavell-While, 'Fritz Haber and Carl Bosch – Feed the World,' The Chemical Engineer, March 1, 2010, https://www.thechemicalengineer.com/features/cewctw-fritz-haber-and-carl-bosch-feed-the-world/.

32. 'Introduction to Ammonia Production,' American Institute of Chemical Engineers, last

modified September 2016, https://www.aiche.
org/resources/publications/cep/2016/september/
introduction-ammonia-production.

33. Jutta Dick, 'Clara Immerwahr,' Jewish Women: A Comprehensive Historical Encyclopaedia, Jewish Women's Archive, retrieved February 20, 2020, https://jwa.org/encyclopedia/article/immerwahr-clara.

34. Joule-Thomson effect
When a gas drops from a high pressure to a lower pressure in a closed system, the temperature drops. All real gases (except hydrogen and helium) cool as they expand at normal temperatures and pressures; this phenomenon is often utilised in liquefying gases.

By closed system, I mean where no work is done by the expanding gas and no heat is exchanged.

By normal temperatures and pressures, I mean those conditions in which the Joule-Thomson cooling effect is observed – a wonderfully circular argument. For more tautological fun see Joule(xv), Thomson(xvi) and Grimes(xiv).

35. Ounces
One avoirdupois ounce equals 28.35 grams, although precious metals are often measured in troy (or apoth-ecaries') ounces just to confuse everyone. One troy ounce equals 31.103 grams.

36. Boyle's Law
Boyle's Law tells you that, with all other things constant, the volume of a gas is inversely proportional to the absolute pressure. If you quadruple the pressure, the volume reduces to a quarter. Liquids, on the other

hand, are almost incompressible.

$$P_1V_1 = P_2V_2$$

In Leith, the pressure of both liquid and gas was set by the operating conditions of the spheres, so one kilogram of ammonia gas at three atmospheres occupied about 330 times the volume of one kilogram of liquid ammonia. Which meant that a gas pipe had to be almost twenty times the diameter of a liquid pipe to carry the same mass flowrate at the same pressure.

37. Ammonia liquid in equilibrium with its vapour (VLE chart, Fiona Erskine 2020)

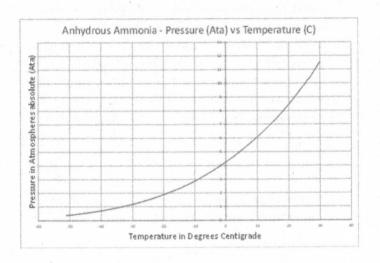

38. Streptomycin

Streptomycin was the first antibiotic cure for tuberculosis (TB), isolated in 1943 in the USA and trialled in the late 1940s.

39. Worth his weight in gold

70kg = 2469 ounces = 2250 troy ounces.
Value of gold in 1988 = £250 per troy ounce.
Value 70kg gold = 2250 x 250 = £562,500.
(Note that in 2020, gold is priced at £1,500 per troy ounce and the same weight would be worth £3,375,000).

www.sandstonepress.com

Subscribe to our weekly newsletter for events information,
author news, paperback and e-book deals, and the occasional
photo of authors' pets!
bit.ly/SandstonePress

 facebook.com/SandstonePress/

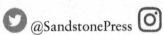 @SandstonePress